Handbook of Reptiles and Amphibians of Florida

PART LIZARDS, TURTLES
TWO & CROCODILIANS

by
Ray E. Ashton, Jr. and Patricia Sawyer Ashton

Drawings by Walter Timmermann

 *Windward* Publishing, Inc.

105 NE 25th St.   P.O. Box 371005   Miami, Fl. 33137

We dedicate this book to our friends and mentors who guided, encouraged, and directed our interest in herpetology over the years, including Ed Halsey, Paul Daniel, Joseph T. Collins, Sheldon Guttman, George T. McDuffie, George Pisani, Jack McCoy, Stan and Jan Roth, Walter Auffenburg, Dick Franz, John Cooper, and the older youths of the Ohio Herpetological Society (now SSAR) that took the time to let one author know he wasn't the only snake lover in the world.

CONTENTS

ACKNOWLEDGEMENTS

The authors wish to express their sincere thanks to the following persons for critically reviewing parts of the manuscript and offering invaluable advice and information: Walter Auffenberg, Archie F. Carr, Roger Conant, John E. Cooper, David M. Dietz, Richard Franz, Dale Jackson, John Iverson, Robert Mount, Wilfred T. Neill, William Palmer, Peter Pritchard, Douglas Simmons, Paul Moler, Larry David Wilson, and Louis Porras.

We would also like to express our thanks to the following for their willingness to provide us with geographic information or data otherwise unavailable: the late Ross Allen and Howard "Duke" Campbell, Alvin Braswell, Gary Bravo, Steve Christman, James Dixon, Neil H. Douglas, William E. Duellman, Harold Dundee, Lewis Ehrhart, Thomas Fritz, Patricia G. Hardline, Donald Hoffmeister, Arnold G. Kluge, Gopher Kuntz, Alan E. Leviton, Barry Mansell, C. J. McCoy, D. Bruce Means, Peter and Ann Meylan, M. C. Mullen, Peter Pritchard, Douglas Rossman, Stanley Roth, Peter Sachs, William Saunders, Sylvia Scudder, L. H. S. Van Mierop, Charles Wharton, John O. Whittaker, Jr., Kenneth Williams, George Zug, and Richard C. Zweifel.

We are also grateful for the artwork provided by Walter Timmermann and for the color slides submitted by the many photographers for use in this book.

PREFACE

Florida has the richest concentration of reptile and amphibian fauna of any state in this country. Its geographic location, climate, varied physiography, and diversity of habitats support 127 native and approximately 25 introduced species. It is an area where the more northern species meet those of the south and the Caribbean, and the western forms converge on the eastern species. This large herpetofauna has made the state a true haven for amateur and professional herpetologists—those who study reptiles and amphibians.

Herpetologists are not the only people who encounter reptiles and amphibians in Florida. Sportsmen in search of record-breaking bass, bird watchers seeking exotic birdlife, or every-day tourists are likely to meet at least one famous reptile during their visit to the state, the American alligator. This spectacular animal is as much a symbol of Florida as are its renowned oranges and famous beaches. In no other state has a reptile attracted so much attention and had so much impact on tourism as the 'gator has in Florida. Each year many thousands of people visit such famous attractions as Ross Allen's Reptile Institute at Silver Springs, which has long featured the alligator in its exhibits and shows.

In addition to alligators, many species of reptiles and amphibians are extremely common and can be seen even in metropolitan areas. The anole inhabits many yards and gardens in the state. New subdivisions, continuously encroaching on once wild areas, include a large array of Florida reptiles and amphibians, often to the dismay of the human inhabitants.

This book has been developed not only for herpetologists, but for those people who visit or live in Florida and are curious about these unusual creatures. It is also intended for students in life sciences, in hopes of providing information about these often misunderstood, feared, and persecuted animals that will lead to a better understanding of their importance in nature.

Toward these ends, an attempt has been made to simplify the scientific information, to limit the use of technical terms, and to write for people with little or no training in biology. We have further tried to answer some of the questions that we know from experience are most often asked by the public.

—R.E.A., Jr. and P.S.A.

HERPETOLOGY IN FLORIDA

In no other state in the country have reptiles and amphibians played so prominent a role in history and development as they have in Florida. For more than thirty years visitors to the state have visited Ross Allen's famous Reptile Institute in Silver Springs. Newspapers, television, and a number of books and movies have contained accounts of the late Ross Allen and his exploits with diamondback rattlesnakes and alligators. Some of the early Tarzan films were made at the Institute, and much of the money provided by the public was used to fund studies by Allen, Wilfred T. Neill, and other herpetologists. The discoveries of these herpetologists attracted numerous others from around the country, and Florida became a mecca for collectors anxious to explore the unique habitats and study their spectacular faunas.

Many visitors eventually came to Florida to study amphibians and reptiles, drawn by less public but even more prominent herpetologists like Archie Carr, famous for his work with sea turtles, Coleman Goin, and others. Earlier herpetological pioneers like Van Hyning, R. F. Deckert, and Thomas Barbour were the first to make detailed reports on the unique herpetofauna found in the state.

Today the list of prominent scientists working on amphibians and reptiles in Florida grows, with such herpetologists as Walter Auffenberg, studying subjects like reptilian fossils and gopher tortoises; Steve Christman, who is studying faunal distributions; D. Bruce Means, who is studying the herpetofauna of the panhandle; Dale Jackson, who studies numerous species of amphibians and reptiles; Peter Pritchard, who is an expert on turtles; Al Schwartz, Tom Hines, Louis Porras, Jay Savage, and Larry Wilson studying a broad spectrum of subjects from Caribbean distributions to rattlesnakes.

Researchers in the field who have studied in Florida but have gone elsewhere to continue their studies include Charles Myers, American Museum of Natural History; Robert Mount, Auburn University; Sam Telford, Jr., International Health Organization; Douglas Rossman, Louisiana State University; William E. Duellman, University of Kansas; Charles Wharton, University of Georgia; Wayne King, Bronx Zoological Gardens, now director at the Florida State Museum; and John Crenshaw, Georgia Institute of Technology, to name a few.

Today many students are actively studying Florida amphibians and reptiles. It will become obvious in the species accounts that there are many things that are unknown and many questions yet to be answered about the state's herpetofauna. We know very little about the day-to-day habits of most species. The little information available on reproduction in many species is only based on captives.

Many worthwhile observations can be made on captive animals if high standards of accuracy are maintained. Information on growth rates, the number, size and weight of young or eggs, breeding, courtship, and longevity are just a few of the types of data that can be obtained. Observations should be recorded on a

6

specimen chart also containing the field collection number, collection date and locality, feeding dates, shedding dates, and other observations.

Field observations on reptiles and amphibians are very difficult and time consuming. One reason why these studies are so difficult is our inability to locate the animal subjects except at certain times. Recently, the development of tiny radio transmitters and the use of radioactive tagging techniques have helped with this major problem. These techniques permit the investigator to locate the animal when it would normally be impossible to find. Once located, observations can be made on microhabitat preferences and the behavior of the animal.

The kinds of information mentioned above and in depth natural history studies conducted in the field are critically important to any type of conservation effort. Without knowledge of specific habitat requirements and the behavior of threatened or endangered animals, conservation efforts can only be superficial at best.

There are still many unanswered questions about the taxonomic relationships of many species. As you look at the photographs and drawings of the turtles you will find that some seem to be quite similar. In fact, scientists continue to question their relationships to each other. Today with new techniques that allow taxonomists to compare chromosomes and even proteins (electrophoresis), a clearer picture of species' relationships can be formed.

Ranges of many species in Florida are not completely delineated. There are areas where ranges of closely related species meet and it is there that taxonomic relationships become uncertain. This brings up the problem of which animals are good "species" or "subspecies", or whether they are simply variations (color, size, pattern).

CONSERVATION

Before the environmental awareness of the 1960's alerted many people to the serious plight of our natural environments and all their inhabitants, most conservationists were mainly concerned about the potential extinction of some birds, mammals, and a few species of fish. Little attention was paid to the plight of reptiles and amphibians. Today, an ever growing list of reptiles and amphibians and their critical habitats are being protected by state and federal laws.

To some people, the increased number of laws governing collecting, maintaining, studying, and importing reptiles and amphibians may seem overly restrictive, serving mostly to supress interest in herpetology on the part of our young people. However, less than 10% of our native reptiles and amphibians are protected; the remainder can be collected and studied without concern for legal restrictions. Many protected species are those that have been the victims of massive habitat destruction and are now limited to only a small percent of their original range. This destruction is the result of land development for agriculture, lumbering, and homesites, and has been so rapid and massive in some areas that the natural habitat has all but disappeared completely. Those natural areas that remain are being increasingly assaulted by masses of people with overland vehicles and dirt bikes, and by camper ghettos, whose occupants move in with little knowledge of, or concern for, the habitats and the living heritage which they contain. Many of them are especially contemptuous of amphibians and reptiles, not hesitating to slaughter harmless and poisonous snakes alike, or to take target practice on sunning turtles or frogs in a pond or lake. To make things worse, some game protectors and other law enforcement officials are unwilling to halt such practices.

Herpetologists, amateurs and professionals alike, can help in the battle to save at least a few islands of natural habitat by educating the general public and increasing their awareness. This can be done by visiting schools, scout troops, and other organizations, using attractive photographs and informing the audiences of the aesthetic appeal and ecological value of these animals. Contempt and disinterest must be converted into curiosity and respect. If more naturalists don't join these endeavors soon, the number of species and their critical habitats that will require protective measures will increase drastically.

Collectors should also maintain a strong conservation ethic in their own herpetological activities. Over-collecting or destroying the habitat can have a drastic effect on local amphibian and reptile populations. Take only those individuals and species as you have a need for and don't collect specimens to sell in the pet trade. Often it is a greater challenge to photograph an animal in its natural habitat than it is to collect it. Finally, don't release exotic species into Florida habitats—the long term effects on native species could be catastrophic.

HERPETOLOGY AND THE LAW

Several state laws relate to collecting and maintaining reptiles and amphibians in Florida. Specific information can be obtained by contacting local game authorities or by writing the Florida Game and Freshwater Fish Commission, Farris Bryant Building, 620 South Meridian Street, Tallahassee, Florida 32304.

Persons interested in collecting or maintaining reptiles and amphibians for research or educational purposes can apply for a scientific collecting permit. This permit is issued on a calendar year basis, and, at the end of the year, a report of collections made must be filed. Young resident Floridians and other Florida amateurs intending to collect or keep a few of the unprotected native reptiles or amphibians for their own study, and not for sale, do not, as the law now stands, need a collecting permit. Out of state visitors, including amateurs, intending to collect in Florida should apply for a permit several months in advance of their collecting trip. Special permits are needed for displaying reptiles or amphibians, and a bond is required for maintaining poisonous reptiles in captivity. Permits do not allow the taking of threatened or endangered species, which include the indigo snake, pine barrens tree frog, American crocodile, all sea turtles, and others, including the protected alligator. Other animals are protected from export or sale, including the gopher tortoise, alligator snapping turtle, and Barbour's map turtle. Without a special permit, there is a possession limit of five gopher tortoises.

The Endangered Species Act of 1973 protects the American crocodile, pine barrens tree frog, Atlantic hawksbill, Atlantic ridley, Atlantic leatherback, indigo snake, Atlantic salt marsh snake, Atlantic green turtle, and Atlantic loggerhead turtle. Several other Florida species are being considered for protection under this act including the short-tailed snake, rim rock crowned snake, and key mud turtle. Others will undoubtedly follow. For details of the federal endangered species law or other pertinent laws, or for information concerning permits to take or study these protected animals, write U.S. Fish and Wildlife Service, P.O. Box 95467, Atlanta, GA, 30347.

Importation of certain reptiles and amphibians into the United States from foreign countries is restricted by international treaties and federal Lacey Act. Before importing exotic species, check with the U.S. Fish and Wildlife Service or with customs officials at Miami International Airport.

There are also state and federal laws against the release of exotic species into the state. Only the Florida Game and Freshwater Fish Commission has the authority to release non-native species in the state.

Herpetology and the Law 9

THE LANGUAGE OF SCIENCE: INTERPRETING TERMINOLOGY AND CLASSIFICATION

Just as we need a name, address, state, and zip code for the postman to locate and deliver a letter to a specific individual among the millions who live in this vast country, scientists need a system to identify individual plants and animal species among the approximately 2 million different species thought to now inhabit the earth. Being able to name and locate individual species does not necessarily indicate the relationships of these species to each other. Locating all the Smiths in the phone book of one town does not tell you if they are related. Just as tracing human geneaology is a complex and often confusing process, so is the system of biological classification, but just as curiosity and often legal necessity causes us to seek our roots amid the complexities of geneaology, the scientist, in order to better understand the biological world, must deal with systems of classification.

HISTORY

The process of developing a usable biological classification system goes back to the ancient Greeks, Aristotle and Theophrastus. Organisms were then classified based on similarity of appearance, or where they lived. Later in the Middle Ages "beastiaries" and "herbals" classified organisms according to their usefullness to man. Many classification systems have been used throughout history but the Swedish scientist Carl von Linné (Linnaeus) set forth a system in his work *Systema Naturae (Classification of Nature)* in 1737 which was the forerunner of the system in use today. Linnaeus grouped organisms according to similarity of structure. He placed all organisms which appeared built alike in the same species and grouped those species which were similar into the same genus. In other words, he placed all horses in the same species and horses and donkeys were in the same genus. Groups of similar genera can then be grouped together into still larger categories.

While our present system of classification was spawned by Linnaeus, certain differences exist. Visible structural similarity alone has been found to be insufficient for accurate classification so many more factors are considered today. Genetics has lent new dimensions to the system of classification. Scientists often disagree on species distinctions and the the way an organism is classified may change as new studies reveal additional information. Linnaeus saw each species as an unchanging, fixed form of life, each member of which was identical in basic structure. The modern view now includes information gained from evolutionary theory and from evidence that there exists a range of natural variation within populations of species. Unlike Linnaeus, modern scientists do not now assume that visual differences necessarily mean different species. Just as few humans look exactly alike, no two members of the same species need appear precisely identical.

SCIENTIFIC NAMES

Linnaeus gave each individual, structurally identical group of organisms a binomial designation (a two-part name), which we now call a scientific name, consisting of two parts, the genus and species. The scientific name of an organism, unlike a common name, is given only to that particular organism and is recognized world wide, regardless of the native language of the person reading it, since all scientific names are in a latinized form, usually composed from Latin or Greek roots. The genus name is always capitalized while the species name is not. Both names are underlined unless they are italicized. When repeating a genus name, the genus may be represented by only the capitalized first letter: *e. g., Terrapene carolina, T. carolina, T. ornata.* Even though not spelled out, the last two names both mean that the genus is *Terrapene (T.).*

Rules of scientific nomenclature are established by international congresses. Scientists strive to follow these rules. However, rules change, and new knowledge is discovered which may change previously believed relationships of organisms, so don't be surprised if texts from different times in history, and even contemporary or future works, use different scientific names or classifications for the same organism. These changes are, however, carefully recorded according to specific rules so that the changes can be traced. Entire books are devoted to listing the synonymies, or other scientific names by which particular organisms have been called.

CLASSIFICATION SYSTEM

The categories of classification which are in use today, beginning with the largest grouping, are KINGDOM, PHYLUM, CLASS, ORDER, FAMILY, GENUS, and SPECIES. Intermediate groupings such as subphylum or subspecies are sometimes inserted. When subspecies names are used the scientific name may have three parts instead of two as in *Terrapene carolina major.*

All turtles are in the kingdom—animalia, phylum—chordata, and class—reptilia. Turtles share the kingdom animalia with all other animals, and the phylum chordata with all fishes, amphibians, other reptiles, birds and mammals, and the class reptilia with the lizards, snakes, and crocodilians. Classes such as reptilia are further divided into orders. The lizards occupy the order squamata which also includes the snakes and the worm lizards (amphisbaenians). The lizards and worm lizards are in the suborder lacertilia. The turtles, terrapins, and tortoises are in the order testudinata, and the crocodiles, alligators and caimans are in the order crocodilia. Orders are further divided into families which are described later in this book (see family accounts). Families are divided into genera, and genera into species.

HOW TO USE THIS BOOK

This book is designed to provide an easy method of indentifying the lizards, turtles and crocodilians found in Florida. By following the easy steps, even a beginner should be able to accurately identify most species.

To identify a specimen, first of all simply leaf through the pictures until you find one resembling your reptile. Read the description, check the key character diagrams, and make note of the habitat and range, comparing them to the location your specimen is from. If the habitat and range do not match, it does not necessarily mean that your specimen is not that species, but it would be wise to continue looking at other species in the book until all possibilities are exhausted. If you have collected a specimen from an area not already marked as part of its range, the specimen and proper collection data would be useful to a museum or university keeping specimens from Florida. (Refer to page 60.) After identifying your specimen, you may wish to place a check by its name in the habitat where it was found on the Species Habitat Chart, pages 53-55.

If you are interested in collecting a particular species, you should read the account and then turn to the Species Habitat Chart to determine the most likely places to find that particular animal. The section on habitats will be useful in understanding the meaning of habitat titles.

THE FLORIDA ENVIRONMENT

The state of Florida, covering approximately 58,560 square miles, offers a variety of habitats for reptiles and amphibians. These habitats are the result of, and are affected by, geologic history, climate, and man's influence.

The Florida peninsula, presently extending from 24.6° to 31° north latitude and from 80° to 87.6° west longitude, has existed as part of a much broader area called the Floridian Plateau since the early Cretaceous period—about 134 million years ago. From the Cretaceous through the Oligocene, the peninsula was separated from the mainland by a seaway, and floodings during the Eocene and Oligocene deposited vast layers of limestone. By the Miocene (25 million years ago) modern Florida made its appearance as a small coral island. More of Florida continued to emerge and it became connected to the continental land mass during the Pliocene, some ten million years ago. Sea level fluctuations during the glacial periods of the Pleistocene (1 million years ago) again submerged much of the Florida peninsula and the receding seas left more deposits. These various sediment depositions have given Florida a great variety of soil types, which in turn support a variety of habitats.

The Florida Environment

So we see that Florida is a physiographically young state with the southern region of very flat land having been above sea level only since the Pleistocene, and some of the eastern coast emerging even more recently. The coastal typography of Florida consists mainly of gently sloping marine terraces which are characterized by a lack of relief resulting in poor drainage. Inland, the largest south Florida lake, Lake Okeechobee, is surrounded by flat marshlands which extend southward into the area known as the Everglades. North of Lake Okeechobee is a hilly region with few areas more than 125 feet (38 m) above sea level, the exception being the Highlands County lake region. Central Florida contains some very hilly areas with elevations as high as 324 feet (99 m) above sea level near Lake Wales in Polk County. Central and north-central Florida are known for their karst topography. Here, the limestone deposited in the geologic past lies close to the surface. The action of water containing dissolved CO_2 on the limestone creates a soluble product that can be carried off. As a result, the limestone is gradually eaten away forming underground waterways, and, where the surface collapses, sinkholes, sinkhole lakes, and caves. As we move north, streams become more frequent and deeper. The northeastern areas contain some freshwater marshlands and again the coastal borders are low and flat, including some saltwater marshes. As you move westward, the topography and soils vary, ranging from the limestone caves at Marianna and the red clays of the Tallahassee region to the white sands and salt marshes of the gulf coastal beaches. On the whole, Florida is drained by a series of rivers, but a central ridge divides the drainage of the peninsula, east from west. Not incidentally should be mentioned the Florida Keys, a series of islands off the tip of Florida. They extend about 135 miles (217 km) south of the mainland and are part of Monroe County, Florida.

Florida is generally known for its southern subtropical and tropical climates. The northern third of the state is warm and temperate. Weather throughout the state is considered mild, especially the weather along the east coast which is tempered by the proximity of the Gulf Stream.

Coastal regions also experience slightly warmer temperatures in the winter and cooler in the summer than inland regions at the same latitude. The mean annual temperature in Florida is in the 70's (20's in degrees Celsius), and almost no part of the state can be considered frost free, though the extreme southern tip of the state and the keys rarely experience freezing temperatures. This may account for the survival and establishment of some tropical species in those southern areas. The rainy season in Florida generally occurs from June to October. Almost all of Florida's precipitation occurs as rain, though it has been known to snow in all parts of the state.

Florida generally has a high relative humidity, because most of the wind patterns which affect Florida must pass over water. Gentle breezes occur almost daily in all places during summer. The prevailing winds come from the east and southeast. Hurricanes generally occur in late summer and early fall and can catastrophically alter Florida habitats.

Man has had an even more catastrophic effect on Florida's natural habitats than have hurricanes. A hurricane's effect may only be temporary; eventually, natural succession will return the land to its former state. Man's damage is often far reaching and irreparable. Man has altered the atmosphere and waterways with his chemical wastes and has altered the landscapes with his pastures, farmlands, buildings, highways, canals and monoculture timberlands. He has wiped out native species and has introduced new ones. The recent introduction of various exotic plants and animals has created problems that were not foreseen. Prime examples are the water hyacinth and hydrilla which choke waterways, and the Australian pine, *Casuarina,* which now thrives and forces out many natural species in south Florida. Recently introduced fish species threaten to displace many of our more desirable game fish. Once gone, the lost species or habitats cannot be replaced. Habitat destruction can occur both directly and indirectly. Habitats may be cut over, built on, or polluted chemically. They can also be destroyed by surrounding them with concrete pavement and buildings which alter wind, temperature, and drainage patterns. Pollution of underground waterways with chemicals and biological wastes can affect habitats hundreds of miles away. Highways and buildings can affect animal populations by cutting across natural migration routes, destroying seasonal breeding grounds or cutting off food supplies.

FLORIDA HABITATS

There are many ways to describe and delineate habitats. We have chosen to divide them into general categories which best reflect differences in suitability for reptiles and amphibians, based on such factors as moisture and type of cover. The habitats roughly correspond to the plant communities for which they are named. Our habitat categories are very broad and by no means describe all the specific plant communities of the state.

Florida Habitats

The most obvious division of habitats is the separation of the aquatic from the terrestrial. In nature, there is generally no clear-cut dividing line, rather, one habitat will blend into another. Aquatic habitats are affected by and affect the terrestrial habitats surrounding them. Certain reptiles or amphibians may occupy an aquatic habitat and the surrounding terrestrial habitats on a regular basis, or only at certain times of the year depending on moisture or breeding season.

The aquatic habitats may be divided as follows: 1. salt marshes, 2. mangrove swamps, 3. freshwater marshes, 4. cypress swamps and domes, 5. gum swamps and river swamps, 6. temporary ponds and roadside ditches, 7. permanent ponds and lakes, 8. small streams and creeks, 9. rivers, and 10. canals. The terrestrial habitats include: 1. pine flatwoods, 2. sand pine-rosemary scrub, 3. longleaf pine-turkey oak sandhills, 4. xeric oak hammocks (dry), 5. mesic hammocks (damp woodland), 6. hydric hammocks (wet woodland), 7. tropical hammocks, 8. temperate deciduous forests, 9. human habitations, golf courses, trash piles, 10. farmlands, fields, disturbed areas, and 11. coastal beaches and dunes.

AQUATIC HABITATS

Salt Marshes: Along the coast of Florida in areas of low relief where fresh-water streams or rivers drain gradually into the ocean and mix with the salt water to form waters of varying salinities, salt marshes can be found. This habitat is characterized by plant species which are tolerant of a variety of intermediate stages between salt and fresh water. Salt marshes appear as extensive plain-like grasslands usually dominated by cord grass *(Spartina)* and salt grass *(Distichlis)* in areas regularly flooded by high tides. The more brackish areas, which may only be seasonally flooded, often support dense stands of rushes *(Juncus roemerianus).* As you move inland into areas where the salt content of the water is lower, the vegetation gradually changes and the salt marsh may eventually merge into a freshwater marsh. Where the salt marsh meets higher ground, the change in vegetation may be abrupt. Islands of trees and dense vegetation may appear to rise up out of the marshy prairie. Deeper channels of open water may wind their way in and out across these grasslands, providing access by boat for the interested explorer. Walking through salt marshes is often quite difficult. The vegetation often has cutting edges or needle sharp points, and the ground generally consists of several feet of mud and decaying vegetation. Salt marshes are most extensive along the southwest and northwest coasts of Florida. In some areas, they may merge with mangrove swamps.

The salinity of the water in the salt marsh habitats presents an insurmountable problem to most amphibians which require freshwater breeding ponds to lay eggs. Some reptiles are able to adapt to this environment and cottonmouths, salt marsh snakes, terrapins, crocodiles, and alligators may be seen.

Mangrove Swamps: Southern Florida coastal areas and much of the Florida Keys are known for their mangrove swamps. These, like the salt marsh, form a transition zone between the salt waters of the ocean and the less salty inland habitats. The mangrove swamp is characterized by the well-known red mangrove *(Rhizophora mangle)* with its arching roots, which anchor it in the shifting sands of areas constantly flooded by ocean tides. Areas farther inland that are more frequently out of water may support growths of the black mangrove *(Avicennia nitida)* with its hundreds of tube-like roots rising out of the mud, and of the white mangrove *(Laguncularia racemose)*. Buttonwood *(Conocarpus erecta)* is another common member of this community and is generally found well above the high tide line. Mangrove swamps are found along the Gulf coast as far north as the Suwannee River, and on the Atlantic coast where they end in northern Brevard county. This fast disappearing habitat forms dense vegetative borders, often merging with salt marshes. The conditions for amphibians and reptiles are similar to the salt marsh community, and the reptile inhabitants are the same as well. However, the woody growth of the mangrove swamp supports a greater diversity, and *Eumeces inexpectatus, Anolis,* and *Elaphe guttata* are commonly found.

Freshwater Marshes: Freshwater marshes occur extensively in Florida and are characterized by soils of low drainage where there is standing fresh water much of the year. There a number of different plant communities which may dominate the areas termed freshwater marshes. The type of vegetation in any given area may be determined by the fluctuation of the water level in that area. The well-known Everglades are a broad expanse of predominantly freshwater marshes which may be dominated by cattails *(Typha),* pickerel weed *(Pontederia),* or maiden cane *(Panicum).* The associated vegetation of freshwater marshes is too diverse to list, but it includes a variety of small trees, shrubs, grasses, and flowering herbs. Freshwater marshes often have pond-like areas of open water or canals winding through them, providing access by boat. Walking in marshes is a muddy job because of the thick layers of mud and peat held in place by thousands of plant roots. Freshwater marshes may be vast expanses of vegetation, or they may only border a lake or pond. They provide excellent moisture and cover for many reptiles and amphibians. Where the marsh meets higher land and drier habitats, the greatest density and variety of organisms may be found. Reptiles and amphibians may move, according to their needs, to the moisture of the marsh or onto the land and its vegetation. Some turtles, snakes, and alligators lay their eggs in the soils of the banks or woodlands. Some frogs, toads, and salamanders move to the waters to lay their eggs, which must remain moist.

Drought and fire are two serious hazards to the marsh. Marshes depend on run-off from surrounding areas, as well as on direct rain, for their water supply. As the state becomes more developed, the drainage patterns are disrupted. Some marshes are intentionally drained to produce more dry land, and others have lost their water into man-made canals. Highways, buildings, and canals all interfere with the normal water flow from the surrounding land into freshwater marshes. One of the greatest freshwater marshes, the Everglades, is endangered by the continuing encroachment of civilization. Interference with drainage from Lake Okeechobee into the Everglades has caused serious droughts in recent years. With droughts often come fires. The years of decaying vegetation held in place by the roots of the sawgrass, hold moisture for a

Florida Habitats

considerable period of time. But when dry, this peat along with the dried surface vegetation, can fuel intense fires that can sweep across the Everglades and through the hammock islands and pinelands that dot the horizon here and there in the vast marsh.

Temporary Ponds and Roadside Ditches: Low areas in pine flatwoods, the bottom of shallow sink holes, or any poorly drained depressions may become temporary ponds in time of heavy rains. These ponds are generally dry most of the year but may support heavy amphibian populations when filled. Roadside ditches frequently fill as well during heavy rains, and, as in temporary ponds, the shallow water generally covers a dense growth of water-tolerant vegetation that is out of water much of the year. This vegetation provides excellent cover for breeding amphibians or for reptiles such as water snakes, which feed upon the amphibians.

Permanent Ponds and Lakes: Natural ponds and lakes are more common in the central and northern part of the state than in the south. Surrounding vegetation may vary greatly from grassy marshes to cypress (Taxodium) or gum (Nyssa) swamps to grassy backyards or cleared sand beaches. The presence of amphibian and reptile populations will depend mainly on the amount of cover available and on the surrounding habitats. Few amphibians or reptiles would be found in the open, deeper waters of the lake. Most would be concentrated in the shallower edge areas with cover. Some lakes or ponds may contain floating aquatic vegetation such as water hyacinth (Eichhornia crassipes), water lilies (Nelumbo lutea), water chinquapin (Nuphar lutea), or water lettuce (Pistia stratiotes). Such vegetation provides additional cover for many amphibians, which may also use the vegetation as convenient perches even far out into the pond or lake. Alligators, turtles, and water snakes are also frequent inhabitants of ponds and lakes.

Cypress Swamps and Domes: Cypress swamps and domes are freshwater areas dominated by cypress trees (Taxodium). The dark, stained waters of these areas are generally shallow, and may dry up during part of the year. In cypress swamps, the muddy ground may support various ferns or hydrophilic plants during the drier periods. Cypress areas (referred to as domes) which tend to be dry for longer periods during the year may support extensive grass and herbaceous floras. When flooded, the grass clumps and other vegetation provide important cover for reptiles and amphibians. Cypress swamps generally cover larger areas than domes. The trees are usually closely spaced, with Spanish moss and other epiphytes hanging from the branches. The dim eerie light beneath the trees and the occasional open pools of dark water have set the scene for many tales of alligators and water moccasins. Cypress domes on the other hand are generally less extensive than swamps. They are roughly circular stands of trees which, if viewed from a distance, form a dome-shaped outline against the horizon. Due to heavy logging of cypress, many of these areas contain stumps and felled trees which form excellent cover for reptiles and amphibians. The shallow water and cover available in cypress areas provide seasonal breeding grounds for many amphibians and reptiles.

Gum Swamps and River Swamps: Located on river flood plains or bottomlands, gum swamps or river swamps are dominated by gum or tupelo trees

Juncus marsh

red mangrove swamp

Florida Habitats

Everglades

roadside ditch　　　　　　　　cypress swamp

Florida Habitats　　　　　　　　　　　　　　　19

(*Nyssa*), and may contain titi (*Cyrilla racemiflora*), sweetbay (*Magnolia virginiana*), and a variety of other trees and shrubs which are tolerant of poorly, drained soils or soils that are seasonally flooded. Dense undergrowth and shade predominate in this habitat. Conditions generally range from moist to very wet throughout the year, which makes this an ideal habitat for many amphibians and snakes which feed on them.

Rivers: Florida is drained by several river systems which are chiefly separated east from west by a high central Florida ridge. Some of the better known river systems include the Suwannee, the St. Johns, the Oklawaha, and the Apalachicola. Rivers may serve as boundaries separating one area or species from another or as corridors of dispersal, bringing species from one area into another. As an example, the Suwannee serves the latter function, bringing many Georgia species into its drainage in Florida. Rivers may be bordered by high ground areas, which are generally hardwood hammocks, or by bottomland river swamp. Rivers may be separated from streams and creeks by their size and depth. Rivers in Florida are often fed by crystal clear springs, and the river may run clear for a time before becoming stained by the acids formed by decaying vegetation.

River banks provide nest sites for turtles. Still water and backwash areas provide suitable sites for amphibians to lay their eggs. At the right time of year, journeying down a Florida river in a canoe will usually result in discovery of water snakes sunning in overhanging branches or turtles sunning on logs.

Small Streams and Creeks: Streams and creeks are usually part of a river drainage system, though they may drain swamps, lakes, ponds, or upland areas. Streams generally maintain a constant flow in one direction. In Florida, stream types may vary from having clear sand bottoms to tanin-rich black water. They are generally shallow and rapid moving, and may flow through a variety of terrestrial habitats. They may contain backwash areas or leaf beds providing suitable habitat for many amphibians.

Some streams contain rooted aquatic vegetation such as pond weeds (*Potamogeton*) and wild celery (*Vallisneria*). Many are densely shaded by overhanging vegetation. Tangles of fallen vegetation, or rocks may provide cover in the stream for a variety of reptile and amphibian inhabitants.

Canals: South Florida, in particular, is criss-crossed with a multitude of man-made canals. These canals were made to drain land so that it could be farmed and developed. They are relatively unwholesome environments, offering little to most reptiles or amphibians and containing little diversity of species.

Canal banks are usually sterile and barren and provide little cover. The water is often silty from run-off and frequently polluted by chemical or biological wastes. Most contain massive growths of slimy algae, bacteria, or waterweeds such as elodea (*Anachris*) or water hyacinth (*Eichhornia crassipes*). Some may contain some rather unusual introduced species of fish. A few frog or turtle species and very often alligators are found in these rather unwholesome canals. Some canals, containing predominantly floating aquatic vegetation and having some bank cover, are more suitable to reptiles and amphibians. These may contain a profusion of turtles, water snakes, or alligators along with various amphibian species.

20

FLORIDA RIVER SYSTEMS

The historic development of the river systems and the period of time in which they have been isolated have given each its own turtle fauna. The greatest number of species or subspecies is found in the Escambia and Perdido rivers of Escambia and Santa Rosa counties. These rivers drain from Alabama and support several more northern and western forms.

Eastward along the panhandle are the Apalachicola and Blackwater rivers, which are biologically very similar systems. They share 12 species or subspecies with the Escambia drainage and the Barbour's map turtle replaces the Alabama map turtle. The Ochlockonee, Econfina and Fenholloway rivers show a great distinction sharing only nine turtle species while having three others shared with the Suwannee and St. Marys river systems.

Major changes in taxa take place at the St. Johns and the remaining peninsular systems. Six of the nine species or subspecies are different forms than those of the panhandle. This is probably due to the segregation of the two areas by the central Florida ridge.

NEAL F. EICHHOLZ and WALLACE HUGHES

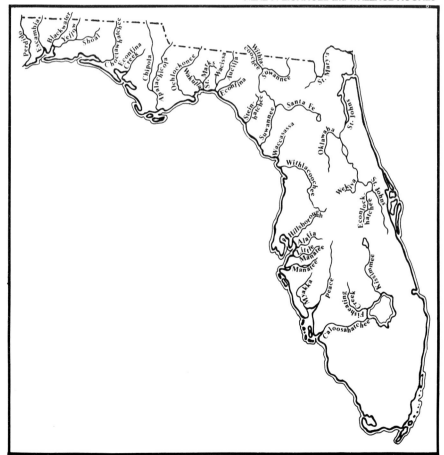

cypress dome pond natural lake

spring fed river

Florida Habitats

stream through mesic hammock

mesic hammock

Florida Habitats

TERRESTRIAL HABITATS

Pine Flatwoods: This habitat is characterized by longleaf pine species (predominantly *Pinus palustris, Pinus serotina,* or *Pinus elliottii*) which occupy land of relatively low relief, usually in areas of poor drainage. Freshwater marsh, pond, or lake habitats may be associated with pine flatwoods, and cypress domes are often scattered as isolated islands throughout the flatwoods. Pine flatwoods generally have well spaced trees with various kinds of understory shrubs. Saw palmetto *(Serenoa repens),* gallberry *(Ilex glabra)* and wax myrtle *(Myrica cerifera)* are the most common. Flatwoods offer a great variety of wild flowers in spring and fall.

Pine flatwoods habitat can also include the monoculture pinewoods planted by man. In monoculture pine, the trees are obviously planted in evenly spaced rows. The understory vegetation is the same as stated above.

Pine flatwoods are a fire adapted community. This means that without fire, the community would, over a period of years, become unsuitable for the species that presently live there. Fire in these communities is a natural occurrence, generally started by lightning before the presence of man. The thick layer of pine needles on the forest floor and the various ground cover fuel a relatively light fire which helps maintain the community by opening up the understory and germinating certain kinds of seeds.

This habitat provides important cover for many amphibians during the part of the year that they are not in breeding ponds. Excellent cover is provided here for reptiles as well.

Sand Pine and Rosemary Scrub: This habitat is dominated by sand pine *(Pinus clausa)* and rosemary *(Ceratiola ericoides).* This plant association is found on light colored, well-drained soils usually on high ground. The trees are widely spaced. The understory is relatively open, and the ground is covered with a variety of low herbs, lichens, and wild flowers. This habitat is most frequent in the center of the state. Standing water is relatively scarce in this habitat, and neither the soil nor vegetation seem to hold much water or produce a high microclimate humidity. Lack of moisture makes amphibians relatively scarce though some make use of the gopher tortoise burrows, pocket gopher *(Geomys)* burrows, and occasional small ponds where the moisture levels are greater in this habitat. Reptiles are common, including a great variety of lizards, snakes, and of course, gopher tortoises.

Longleaf Pine-Turkey Oak Sandhills: Dominated by longleaf pine *(Pinus palustris)* and turkey oak *(Quercus laevis),* this community is usually found on high, well-drained, sandy soils. The trees are widely spaced with open grassy areas between. Wire grass *(Aristida stricta)* is the common ground cover. Understory shrubs include saw palmetto *(Serenoa repens),* and pawpaw *(Asimina).* This is also a fire adapted community. Open water is not common. Amphibians may make use of gopher tortoise burrows where the humidity is higher. Reptiles are common where there is good cover.

24

Florida's Changing Pinelands: Both the sand pine-rosemary scrub and the longleaf pine-turkey oak communities have been greatly damaged by man in the state of Florida. Their location on high, dry soils makes them ideal for housing developments and for citrus farming. Much of the virgin pine land of the state has been cut over at least once by 1930. Most pinelands in existence today are areas where pine has regenerated. Citrus groves have replaced many of these pine communities in central and southern Florida. Unfortunately, citrus groves lack the necessary habitat requirements for the reptiles and amphibians that occupied the pine communities, and, consequently, citrus groves support few of them.

Xeric Oak Hammock: Found on relatively dry, sandy soils, that generally were once occupied by pine, the xeric oak hammock is dominated by several species of oak including turkey oak *(Quercus laevis)*, blue jack oak *(Quercus incana)*, southern red oak *(Quercus falcata)*, and live oak *(Quercus virginiana)*. The trees are usually well spaced and the ground is generally grassy, with a variety of flowering herbaceous plants in sunny areas. Standing water is uncommon in this habitat, though an occasional shallow pond may be present. Amphibians are less common in this habitat because of the general lack of moisture. A variety of reptiles, including gopher tortoises are present.

Mesic Hammocks (Damp Woodland): This woodland of moderate moisture is characterized by the presence of southern magnolia *(Magnolia grandiflora)*, and laurel oak *(Quercus laurifolia)*, along with a variety of other tree species including blue-beech *(Carpinus caroliniana)*, hophornbeam *(Ostrya virginiana)*, flowering dogwood *(Cornus florida)*, and American holly *(Ilex opaca)*. Typically the mesic hammock has three vegetation layers: an overstory of large tall trees, an understory of smaller trees and shrubs, and the ground over of grasses, herbaceous plants and lower shrubs. Shade predominates and the vegetation forms tangled thickets tied together by green-briers *(Smilax)* and grape vines *(Vitis)*. Streams may wind through the hammock, or the canopy may open around a small pond. The conditions in the hammock are moderate throughout the year. The dense vegetation protects the hammock from drying winds and from temperature extremes. The moist, moderate conditions are ideal for many reptiles and amphibians.

Hydric Hammock: These low, flat woodlands are subject to periodic flooding. The trees may include a variety of water-hardy species such as water oak *(Quercus nigra)*, sweet gum *(Liquadambar styraciflua)*, winged elm *(Ulmus alata)*, hackberry *(Celtis laevigata)*, willow *(Salix nigra)*, and box elder *(Acer negundo)*. These thick woods surround streams and river bottoms. The habitat is variable; part of the year it is dry with leaf litter on the ground, and then is wet and muddy during other times. This provides ideal habitat in terms of moisture and cover for many reptiles and amphibians.

pine flatwoods

longleaf pine-turkey oak sandhills, wire grass

xeric oak hammock

Florida Habitats

flatwoods pond

sand pine scrub

Florida Habitats

Tropical Hammock: This category includes a variety of southern Florida hammocks. They are composed mainly of a variety of tropical plant species, which form dense canopies of vegetation, and relatively open hammock floor covered with layers of rotting vegetation and ferns. Lianas (large vines) are common and give this habitat its typical "tropical" appearance. Epiphytes (air plants) such as orchids, bromeliads, mosses, and lichens may cover the tree limbs. The tree species include predominantly evergreen, non-coniferous hardwoods such as gumbo-limbo *(Bursera simaruba),* pigeon-plum *(Coccoloba diversifola),* mahogany *(Swietenia mahogani),* poisonwood *(Metopium toxiferum)* and strangler fig *(Ficus aurea).*

These hammocks may be found as isolated highlands in the middle of wet prairies like the Everglades, or some still remaining protected areas along the tip of Florida and on a few keys. They occupy higher limestone outcroppings. Most of this type of habitat has been destroyed by large scale building in south Florida that started in the 1920's.

This habitat is also endangered in south Florida by the introduction of Australian pine *(Casuarina equisetifolia)* and melaleuca *(Melaleuca).* These trees have begun to slowly replace the dominant hammock species along hammock borders or where trees have been weakened or destroyed by fire.

Temperate Deciduous Forest: This is the common deciduous forest of the eastern United States, north of Florida. The relief is typically hilly and the soil is well drained. The forest floor is generally covered with a layer of dead leaves and decaying vegetation. In the spring and summer, ferns and wild flowers dot the ground beneath the shade of these broad-leafed trees. Streams may wind through the forest, or the canopy may open onto a field, grassland, or farm pond. The dominate tree species generally include oaks *(Quercus),* hickories *(Carya),* elm *(Ulmus),* maple *(Acer),* basswood *(Tilia),* tulip poplar *(Liriodendron tulipifera),* beech *(Fagus grandifolia),* and walnuts *(Juglans).* Temperate deciduous forests are found in northern peninsular Florida and in the panhandle. The conditions for reptiles are good, particularly where there is good cover such as fallen logs. Amphibians that require water to breed are found near streams or temporary ponds that may form after heavy rains. Salamanders which breed under moist logs and leaf litter may also be found. This habitat is where northern species such as the copperhead make their intrusion into Florida.

Human Habitation, Golf Courses, Trash Piles: In Florida, human developments have produced their own habitats for reptiles and amphibians. Some examples we are all familiar with are the snake in the woodpile, the frog eggs in the bird bath, or the tree frog on the window sill. Lights around buildings and street lamps attract insects, which in turn attract insect eating amphibians such as tree frogs and toads. Golf course lights and ponds provide a perfect combination for frogs and toads—moisture and insect-attracting lights.

Another by-product of human existence is trash. Trash piles are unique in their attractiveness to various reptiles and amphibians. Many articles found on trash piles such as mattresses, refrigerators, sofas, and cardboard boxes hold moisture long after soaking rains, so they provide excellent moisture and cover. A variety of reptiles and amphibians may be found, depending on the habitat surrounding the trash pile location.

Coastal Beaches and Dunes: Beaches and dunes generally consist of expanses of sand bordered by the ocean on one side and by dune forests, open fields, human habitations, or roads on the other. The type of associated coastal vegetation depends on the location of the particular beach or dune. In general, the vegetation has special adaptations such as waxy, succulent leaves to prevent water loss, or secretory glands to eliminate excess salt. Most vegetation must also be adapted to salt spray and possible inundation by salt water. Typical species include sea purslane *(Sesuvium)*, seaside pennywort *(Hydrocotyle bonariensis)*, sea oats *(Uniola paniculata)*, railroad-vine *(Ipomoea)*, camphorplant *(Heterotheca subaxillaris)*, saw palmetto *(Serenoa repens)*, and salt bush *(Baccharis hamilifolia)*.

pond surrounded by hydric hammock

strangler fig in tropical hammock

deciduous forest—upper panhandle

Florida Habitats

human habitat—remains of old house

coastal dunes and beaches

Florida Habitats

CAPTURING REPTILES

A major "rule" of reptile collecting, indeed all animal collecting, is to learn to identify protected species and to leave them alone. If you have legitimate reasons for collecting them, you may be able to obtain a permit from the appropriate state and federal agency to take a certain species. These permits are not issued without good cause however, and general or commercial collectors will be denied. Some species which are not necessarily designated as protected may have certain restrictions on the numbers which may be taken by collectors. See the section on "Herpetology and the Law". Of course, a good conservation principle is to never collect more animals than you have a real need for. Wholesale collecting and selling animals to pet or hide dealers is not a legitimate excuse for collecting large numbers of animals and is in some cases illegal.

Many reptiles live within a more or less definite area called a home range. Inside this area are logs, leaf litter, or other types of cover which constitute the animal's microhabitat. If collectors destroy this microhabitat, they may cause the loss of many unnoticed animals. Cover which has been turned in search of reptiles should be replaced when possible. It may take many years for natural processes to replace habitat and a devastated area is worthless for collecting as well as being less suitable for its inhabitants.

COLLECTING LIZARDS

Very few species are found in all habitats, so refer to the Florida habitat species charts and read the species accounts for those animals you are seeking before taking to the field. The time of year and time of day are important for many species. When it is too hot or cold, reptiles are not likely to be easily found. When the sun is strong and temperatures high, it is best to collect in the cooler hours of the morning or late afternoon as the sun is setting. The opposite is true when the weather is generally cool.

Despite efforts by local officials and conservationsts, people still persist in dumping trash on the back roads of the state. Though unsightly, these trash piles, allowed to age a year or so, are ideal collecting sites for many reptiles, especially if sheet metal, boards, stoves or similar large, flat-surfaced items of cover are among the refuse. The combination of cover and insects, rodents, and other food attract many species, including lizards, rat snakes, king snakes and rattlesnakes. Old abandoned houses with building materials scattered about also make excellent collecting sites. Be sure that the premises are abandoned before disturbing anything. The rights of property owners must always be respected.

Heavy-soled shoes and gloves should be worn when collecting in these areas to prevent injury from rusty nails, broken glass, and other sharp objects. A heavily constructed potato rake is ideal for lifting cover or tearing trash apart.

COLLECTING EQUIPMENT

Most lizards can be easily caught by a quick hand. Nearly all lizards in Florida have tails that break easily so avoid grabbing that anatomical portion. Fossorial lizards, like mole and sand skinks, can be collected by digging through the loose soil of pocket gopher or gopher tortoise mounds using a broad-bladed potato rake. This should be done early in the morning when the sand is being warmed by the sun, but before it gets too hot. During the winter, it may take until midday before the sand is warm enough to make these mounds attractive basking areas.

Many lizards can be collected under bark or piles of trash and boards, especially five-lined skinks and fence lizards. During the winter months in the northern part of the state, anoles, skinks and others can be found hibernating in rotting logs, stumps, and sawdust piles. The potato rake is useful for turning the trash and boards and breaking up logs and stumps.

Anoles, fence lizards, and to some degree, racerunners can be collected using a slip noose. Tie a slip-knot loop made of light monofilament fishing line or waxed dental floss to the end of a telescoping cane pole or a thin twig. The loop should slip easily and should not be much larger than the target lizard species' head. With a slow steady motion the loop is slipped over the lizard's head and pulled tight with a quick up and back motion. Lizards are rarely harmed by this technique since their scales generally prevent injury.

An old fashioned rubber band gun or a rubber band shot from the fingers does an excellent job of stunning lizards. With practice the correct size rubber bands and appropriate force can be determined so that the lizard will be temporarily stunned but not squashed by the shot. Serious target practice is recommended before attempting this method in the field.

A similar method involves using a sling shot with grapes as ammunition. Though equally as effective as the rubber band ammunition, the grapes may cause more trauma to the lizard from the impact, and later from the sticky juice. The proper technique of pulling back the sling with the grape seated can be learned with practice. Be sure to wash the lizard immediately after capture.

Collectors wanting specimens for preservation may find that using a pistol or rifle (22 cal.) with dust shot is the most efficient method when live specimens are not desired. This method is not recommended when collecting lizards for use as food for snakes, due to the possible residual dust in the carcass.

lizard noose

Drift fences and can pit traps are also excellent ways to collect live lizards. These can be constructed from relatively inexpensive materials such as aluminum flashing or thin sheet metal, a few stakes and pieces of plywood or board, and some gallon cans. Stakes are used to support the flashing or sheet metal in an upright position perpendicular to the ground. This forms a fence. This fence should be between 20 and 30 feet long and should be placed between two environments in a locality where movement of desired species is known to occur. The bottom of the fence should extend one to two inches below the surface. The gallon cans should be buried flush with the surface of the ground at the center of either side of the fence and at either end. Small stones placed along the top of the can will support a piece of plywood or board which is just large enough to cover the can opening while still allowing enough of an opening to let the lizards in. This cover will protect the captives in the can from direct sunlight and from heavy rainfall. Traps should be checked daily since specimens left in traps for longer periods will starve or expire from heat or cold.

COLLECTING TURTLES

Many species of turtles can be collected as they cross roadways. This of course is a rather haphazard method of collecting since it is difficult to say when turtles are going to move. Box turtles, more predictable than most, usually move early in the morning.

Many species of aquatic turtles can be caught with baited hook just off the bank, or on trotlines. Chicken gizzards, chunks of beef or fish are commonly used as bait. This method is particularly effective for snapping turtles.

In clear waters, snorkeling is an effective way to locate and collect turtles.

There are numerous methods of trapping aquatic turtles. Box traps (made of ¼" hardware cloth) or hoop traps (made of 1" mesh cord net) with funnel openings are very effective when baited with carrion. If these traps are used, remember to leave the top part of the trap above the water line so the turtles can come up to breathe, or they will drown in a very short period of time.

Another type of aquatic turtle trap is the barrel or basking trap. This can be used with herbivorous turtles that can't be stimulated to enter a baited trap. There are several versions of this trap—the simplest is a smooth-sided barrel or can, wide enough for the desired size of turtle. It should be set so that the rim of the barrel is just above the surface of the water and weighted in place (see illustration). A two-by-four board is placed across the center of the can or barrel. The trap should be placed next to a favorite basking log. The turtles will use the new "log" but when they drop off, they will land in the can or barrel. A more effective version of this trap is made by counterbalancing the basking board so that a turtle's weight will cause the board to dip into the can. Once the turtle falls, the board will rise back into place ready for the next basker.

All traps can be extremely effective and require that the trapper be conscientious in checking the traps daily and in removing the traps when collecting is finished. One author found a cage trap with 22 dead (drowned) turtles that had been left for a considerable time by a trapper. Traps should be used for mark and recapture or other legitimate studies. Some traps can only be used by special permit from the Florida Fish and Game Commission.

Capturing Reptiles

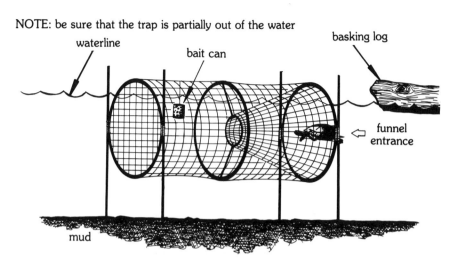

NOTE: be sure that the trap is partially out of the water

waterline

bait can

basking log

funnel entrance

mud

aquatic turtle trap

PHOTOGRAPHY

Wildlife photography has become a major hobby in the United States, and many herpetologists have found it as enjoyable to photograph amphibians and reptiles in the wild as to collect them. Also, photographs of habitats and animal behavior taken on field trips may prove to be valuable.

Most reptiles are rather small and require close-up lenses and flash or strobe equipment for good results. Some are difficult to approach and telephoto lenses are required. It is often advantageous to capture the subject and pose it under the right lighting conditions. Many amphibians and reptiles will eventually tire and calm down long enough to be posed in the desired stance. Success in this endeavor requires considerable patience, but the rewards are well worth the time spent.

PHOTOGRAPHING LIZARDS

When photographing lizards, be very careful not to handle or restrain the animal by the tail. Many lizards have "break away" tails. When posing the lizard, be sure that the eyes are open and the head is erect. Toes should be extended. Once the basic body pose is obtained, changes in appendages can be made using a pencil or small stick to move the desired part with a slow, even motion, without frightening the animal. The best results will be obtained if the animal is looking toward or slightly to either side of the camera.

PHOTOGRAPHING TURTLES

With the possible exception of large snakes, turtles are by far the most difficult of the reptiles to photograph. Shy specimens refuse to extend the head and legs, while the less shy tend to continue to crawl away. Photographing either will require considerable patience. One method of photographing aquatic turtles is underwater. A 10 gallon aquarium with clean unscratched glass and clean water works well. The best bottom is thoroughly washed sand or natural gravel. Washed aquatic vegetation and waterlogged leaves will add to the natural look. Dual flash or photo lights should come from the top and sides to eliminate shadows.

When posing turtles on land, be sure that their shells are clean and kept moist. This will allow the color pattern on the scutes to show. Also, be sure the head, neck, and front legs are extended to show markings.

FIELD NOTES

Valuable information can be obtained from field notes made on collecting trips and logs kept on specimens maintained in captivity. Many field collectors keep a loose-leaf notebook of standard size, while others use a pocket-sized or clipboard type. In any case, notes should be kept in chronological order. Specimens collected should be assigned a field number which is entered into the notes and also placed on the specimen tag, or feeding chart accompanying the

REA FIELD NOTES   p 1109

17 SEPTEMBER 1975 MONROE COUNTY - FLORIDA KEYS
Weather: Clear, low 72°F high 87°F, slight
            westerly breeze, barometric pressure high.
Participants: Dick Franz, Pat Ashton

Notes: From Pigeon Key we traveled to Big
Pine Key to collect reptiles and to locate
potential amphibian call sites for night
collecting. Odometer reading 50732.1. Drove
via US1 to ST RT 292 and side roads to
Co. RD. 6292 to Key Deer Wildlife Refuge.

Locality: Fla, Monroe Co, Big Pine Key, 1 mi
W of inters. US 1 and ST RD 292 on north
side of 292

Collected: Field Tag. No.
         REA 10B-1014 Diadophis punctatus
                1015 Cnemidophorus sexlineatus
                      Anolis sagrei observed

    Specimens collected in old board pile in
pinewoods. Observed birds: white-crowned pigeons,
gray kingbird, Bahama swallow

Locality: Fla, Monroe Co., Key Largo, .5 mi NE
1 mi So. intersect of US 1 and ST RD 905,

Collected: 1016— 2 Sphaerodactylus notatus
           1017

typical entry in field notes log

animal. The data in the note book should be complete, concise, and include the following: date, locality (*i.e.* state, county, road or waterway, air distance from nearest post office or map coordinates), species collected in that locality, specimen field number, collector(s), type of habitat and microhabitat, and weather conditions.

Additional information such as routes traveled, distances, expenses, times, and other activities, and a summary of your observations may be valuable in the future. The information you omit may someday be the information you need.

MAINTAINING LIZARDS IN CAPTIVITY

Most native lizards are relatively easy to maintain in captivity. All require a dry, well ventilated cage to avoid dermal and respiratory diseases. Screen topped aquaria, 10 gallon or larger, are excellent vivaria for lizards. Sand or wood chip substrates allow the lizards a place to burrow. Tree bark or similar light weight material should be provided for cover. Water should be supplied in a small dish with clean rocks placed in it. These allow wet surface areas where the lizard may lap water, and they keep crickets and other live food out of the water so they don't drown before they can be consumed. Many lizards lap water from leaves or other surfaces. A light morning sprinkle will best provide such captives with water.

Lizards require areas where they can bask. They need temperatures around 90° F (32° C) in the basking areas while the rest of the cage should be 75-80° F (24-27° C). The light source, such as a gro-lux or other plant growing light, should give off ultra violet light. Basking lights should be on timers or turned on and off at times comparable to normal day length for the time of year. Photoperiod, length of exposure to light, may become important when planning to breed lizards. Research the normal temperature regime and photoperiod of the lizards' natural habitat if breeding is intended.

use pegboard in lieu of wire

light is used for providing heat in basking area

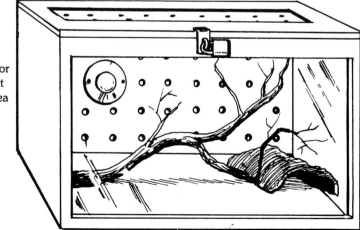

lizard cage

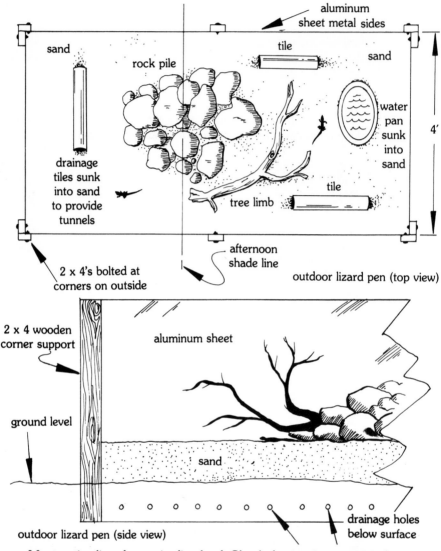

aluminum sheet metal sides

sand

tile

rock pile

sand

drainage tiles sunk into sand to provide tunnels

water pan sunk into sand

4'

tile

tree limb

afternoon shade line

2 x 4's bolted at corners on outside

outdoor lizard pen (top view)

2 x 4 wooden corner support

aluminum sheet

ground level

sand

drainage holes below surface

outdoor lizard pen (side view)

Most native lizards require live food. Check the species accounts for unique dietary requirements, but in captivity most lizards will eat live crickets, grasshoppers, and other arthropods. Mealworms should be used sparingly as food. A vitamin-mineral supplement should be provided to long term captives. This can be supplied by dusting food items with the supplement.

Avid lizard collectors may choose to keep their captives outdoors in pens. These can be constructed in a way to allow excellent behavioral observations. The walls should be of sheet metal or any other smooth surfaced material and should be buried 8-10″ in the ground. Soil within the enclosure should be well drained. Artificial burrows, basking areas and tree branches should be included. Avoid overcrowding since lizards can be very territorial.

MAINTAINING TURTLES IN CAPTIVITY

Until the mid 1970's, baby turtles were sold in every five and dime store, pet shop and at every fair. Public health officials changed that when they discovered that baby turtles often carried salmonella. This bacteria can cause severe gastric and intestinal distress and occasionally death, particularly in children. The possibility of contracting the disease increases when the water in the turtle's bowl is fouled with excess food and feces. Extreme caution should be taken to maintain turtles in a clean environment and to be sure that children wash their hands immediately after handling or cleaning their pets.

Turtles and tortoises can make excellent long term pets for those who take appropriate care of them. We recommend that youngsters that are infatuated with a newly discovered turtle be allowed to observe and maintain it for a day or two and then be encouraged to release it where it was found.

Aquatic turtles can be best maintained in an aquarium that is tilted so that there is water at one end and a dry area at the other. A plant growing spotlight directed at the dry end should be set to raise the temperature to 85-90° F (30-32° C). Like lizards, turtles require ultra violet light for proper growth and health. The basking light should be turned off at night. Check the species accounts for general food habits of your specimen. Most small turtles require protein, calcium, and phosphorus for growth, particularly of the shell. The authors have found that high protein commercial fish food pellets used for rearing trout and catfish are excellent for captive turtles. This food is well balanced and includes vitamin and mineral supplements. We also feed them chicken necks which have been chopped into small pieces with a cleaver and have the vertebrae crushed with a hammer. Whole fish, like minnows or smelt, are also excellent turtle food. Flaked fish food available in most pet stores is not adequate food for turtles.

Turtles, particularly large ones, can also be maintained in oblong cattle tanks tilted and set up just like the aquarium previously described. These tanks usually have a drain valve at one end which makes them very easy to clean. If kept outside, be sure the turtles can get out of the sun and that there is an overflow designed to allow excess rain water to drain off before the tank overflows or the inhabitants drown.

Gopher tortoises are not recommended as pets for amateurs. They require a complex vegetarian diet although they will graze on grass, fruits and vegetables. Do not feed them lettuce. Lettuce is of little nutritional value and seems to be almost addictive to the tortoise. Tortoises require drinking water and also should be sprayed with water occasionally or allowed to soak. They generally should be kept in a dry environment with a place to hide or burrow, and which is kept warm throughout the year. Tortoises do best at temperatures above 70° F (21° C), even in the winter. They are particularly prone to respiratory infections in winter, or at any time they become too cool or wet.

Box turtles do well in captivity and have relatively simple requirements. They require a pan of water that they can occasionally soak in and a basking area. They are omnivorous as adults and will eat fruits, worms, and canned cat or dog food (which provide vitamins and nutrients). Box turtles also love those pesky slugs you find in your garden, but be careful not to give than any that may have

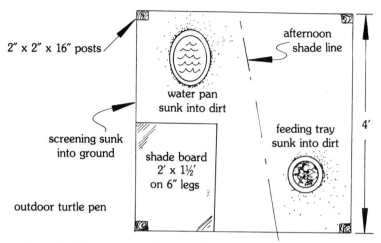

2″ x 2″ x 16″ posts

afternoon shade line

water pan sunk into dirt

screening sunk into ground

feeding tray sunk into dirt

shade board 2′ x 1½′ on 6″ legs

4′

outdoor turtle pen

been poisoned with slug erradicators. Juvenile box turtles, under 3″, are carnivorous and should be fed cat or dog food, worms, slugs, crickets, and other similar arthropods.

We recommend a converted sand box or other similar enclosure made up of 1″ x 8″ boards sunk into the ground at least 1″ and placed in the yard as an excellent box turtle habitat. Place some leaf mulch in the shaded end so they can burrow into it when it becomes too hot or cold. Enclosures do not do well when placed over cement, even if the floor is covered with sand, since the substrate may become much too hot for the turtle due to heat transfer from the concrete.

Avoid dropping turtles on pavement or hard floors. Despite the fact that the shell of some turtles may even withstand the force of an alligator's jaws, they will crack like eggs when dropped. Painting a turtle's shell or carving initials into it can kill the turtle. The shell is a living, growing part of the turtle's body.

STUDYING LIZARDS AND TURTLES

Lizards and turtles can provide easy and interesting subjects for behavioral studies. Most areas around buildings and yards that have not been overly sprayed with pesticides or that are not overrun by cats will have fair sized populations of anoles and other lizards. Anoles are easily observed and can be captured using the noose technique. Lizards can be humanely marked using latex paint or fingernail polish. Small dots or numerals should be made on the back of each lizard and a record kept.

A map of the study area should be made and every time a marked individual is sited or recaptured, the location is noted on the map. From this information, the student can determine home range and population size and structure.

Similarly, turtles can be captured and marked, and then recaptured. Marking can be done by notching the edge of the shell with a nail file or triangular file. By establishing a numbering system based on location of notches on the scutes, a large number of individuals can be marked. Growth rates and population dynamics can be studied using these methods.

Capturing Reptiles

NATURAL HISTORY

CROCODILIANS

ORIGINS

The crocodilians had their beginning in the Jurassic. In the Cretaceous they developed into forms similar to those we find today. The 22 species of crocodilians found on the earth today are a bare remnant of the number that existed in the past. The crocodilian ancestors were in the subclass archosauria, or the "ruling reptiles" of the Mesozoic Era. The alligators and crocodiles are the closest living reptile relatives of the dinosaurs; their closest living relatives are the birds. The largest fossil crocodilian is *Phobosuchus* which attained a length of more than 45 feet.

Crocodilians have several features that differentiate them from other reptiles. The stomach is divided into two sections, similar to birds. The front section has developed into a grinding organ called a gizzard. Alligators and crocodiles swallow stones which grind food in the gizzard, as do some birds. Another higher vertebrate characteristic possessed by the crocodilians is a heart that allows oxygenated blood coming from the lungs to remain separated from the deoxygenated blood returning from the body. In the other reptiles the head is three chambered, allowing the blood to mix, and is less efficient. The crocodilian heart is very similar to the four chambered heart found in mammals and birds.

Crocodilians all have bony skulls and snouts with teeth around the perimeter of the jaw. The eyes, nostrils, and ears are arranged on the top of the skull. Air is carried from the nostrils through a tube-like structure over a bony palate in the roof of the mouth. The nostrils and ear openings have flaps or valves that are closed when the animal dives. The eye has two eyelids: the inner eyelid is transparent and protects the eye underwater. The presence of a nictitating membrane is a trait also shared by birds.

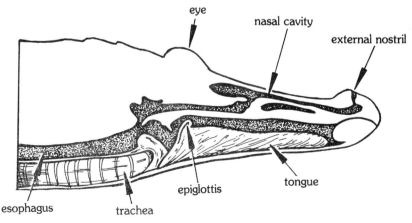

crocodilian head and breathing parts

The dorsal scales—and in some caimans and crocodiles, the belly scutes—have underlying protective bony plates. These bony plates are absent in the alligator. All species have long muscular tails that are used as the main drive in swimming.

LOCOMOTION

Crocodilians have two methods of movement on land. They can move slowly for some distance or quite rapidly for short distances by slithering on their bellies. They shove with all four five-toed feet. It is this motion that they use when sliding into the water after sunning on a bank. To walk any distance, crocodilians lift themselves up on all four legs in a stance similar to mammals and not at all like lizards and salamanders. Alligators have been known to walk several miles using this technique. When walking, the limbs work in unison to effect a gait. But, alligators can gallop, with the legs working in pairs to give maximum thrust, while the tail and body swing side to side in pendulum fashion. Speeds up to 6-8 miles per hour can be maintained for short distances by the smaller adults.

Crocodilians are highly aquatic and have many adaptations for this life. They can swim very rapidly for a short time and can cruise indefinitely using the sculling motion of the muscular tail. The feet are pressed to the sides while swimming, and are used for balance, and on occasion, as rudders.

SENSES

Smell: Crocodilians are not noted for a keen sense of smell and this sense does not appear to play a major role in obtaining food, especially underwater. Since there are glands present under the throat of crocodilians, it is presumed that odors or pheromones play an important social function.

Hearing: Crocodilian hearing appears to be rather well developed. Female crocodilians respond to the croaking danger calls of their young for some distance. Vocalizations already described play an important role in crocodilian society.

The ears are located behind the eye and above the point where water would interfere with airborne sounds when the animal is sitting or cruising at the water's surface. When submerged, a valve or flap of skin covers the ear opening automatically. Sounds underwater are probably "felt" by the entire body.

Sight: The sense of sight in crocodilians is well developed. The eye has a vertical pupil which is that of a nocturnal animal. When diving, the eye is covered with a nictitating membrane which protects the eye and allows the animal to see underwater. A second set of eyelids, similar to those in other vertebrates, close the eyes. Crocodilians are noted for reflective "eye shine". At night, when a light is shone into the eye of a crocodilian, light is reflected back from the retina, in a manner similar to a dog or cat. In alligators the eye shine is reddish.

Touch and Heat: The armored crocodilian has a remarkably acute sense of touch. Attesting to this, the female will gently uncover a nest of young, rarely causing any damage to them. She may also gently pick the hatchlings up with her powerful jaws and maneuver them into her gut or pouch. She then takes them to the water where she releases them.

OBTAINING FOOD

Crocodilians are predators. After the yolk has been absorbed by the hatchling, it begins its predatory life by eating snails, aquatic insects and crustaceans. As it grows it graduates into feeding on other things such as tadpoles and fish, but invertebrates play a key role in the diet for the first year.

Large alligators feed on fish, frogs, turtles, reptiles and birds. There have been reports of very large crocodilians feeding on hoofed livestock and there is some indication that they will attack dogs.

Crocodilians have jaws that have very powerful muscles for closing down on prey. In fact, a large alligator with its peg-like teeth can provide the several hundred pounds per square inch pressure needed to crack the shell of a turtle. Prey is usually taken at or in the water. The prey is crushed or shredded by a thrashing motion. The crocodilian can hold the prey in its mouth underwater because there is a flap or valve that covers the throat when the animal is submerged. If the prey is small enough, it is swallowed whole; if it is too large, it is crushed, pulverized, and ripped into smaller pieces. In order to swallow, a crocodilian must rise out of the water to avoid flooding the gut and lungs when the valve opens in the throat.

Feeding is done primarily at night, but food is pursued at any time. Although rare, alligator attacks on man happen every year. Developments along lakes and rivers and in other crocodilian habitats in Florida have brought humans and alligators together more frequently. Feeding alligators, or swimming with them during the evening or at night increases the chances of a serious confrontation. However, like snake bite, the chance of such attacks on humans are exaggerated and usually the victim is as much at fault as the alligator or crocodile. Humans are within the food size range for large crocodilians and if they make themselves available in a vulnerable situation at night, hungry crocodilians may consider them fair game. Similarly, nests, which are protected by law, should be left alone since they may be fiercely defended by the attending female and the potential for attack is real.

BEHAVIOR AND REPRODUCTION

Although crocodilians possess very small, primitive brains, they display very complex behavior patterns. Female alligators prepare a mound nest made up of decaying vegetation. The nest is usually built near the edge of the water. Eggs are laid in the nest, covered and guarded by the female. Guarding can be intense, and the female can be very aggressive at times. Similarly, American crocodiles make nests in sandy banks and also guard these nests. In both species the female responds to the croaking grunts made by the hatchlings as they begin to emerge from the eggs. The female digs out the young and may transport them, a few at a time, in her throat pouch to the water. Females continue to respond to the croaks of youngsters for a least a year.

Mature alligators begin mating in the spring. This is marked by the bulls' (males) bellowing. They accomplish these loud and resounding bellows by arching their backs and tails and raising their heads while forcing air over vocal cord-like strands in the esophagus. These vocalizations mark the territories of the males and apparently attract females.

Courtship in both alligators and crocodiles is a tender ritual. Males caress the females with their chins, possibly releasing pheromones from the pair of glands on the underside of the jaw. The male mounts the female, wraps his tail around and under the female so the penis can be inserted into the female's cloaca.

TEMPERATURE REGULATION

Like other reptiles, crocodilians must rely on the environment and behavior to control their temperature. They maintain an optimal temperature by basking in the sun to raise their body temperature, and by retreating to the shade or water to lower it.

Many studies have been conducted on temperature regulation in crocodilians. This interest is due to their size. An adult crocodile or alligator may weigh several hundred pounds and as a result of this size take much more time to raise its temperature than a lizard which might weigh only a few ounces, or a snake that may weigh only a few pounds. These studies have made many biologists speculate on the problems dinosaurs—that weighed up to several tons—may have had in regulating their temperatures. Some scientists have suggested that dinosaurs may not have been cold blooded, but rather warm blooded like their close relatives, the birds.

LIZARDS

ORIGINS

Lizard fossils have been found that date as far back as the Triassic, 220 million years ago, but the earliest known in the United States date only as far back as the upper Cretaceous. In Florida, the earliest known lizard fossil is from the Cretaceous, about 130 million years ago. Although lizards appear to resemble miniature dinosaurs, in fact they are only distantly related. There are records of very large lizards having existed in the United States, some even larger than the modern Komodo dragon. The saurians, or lizards, do resemble the marine mosasaurs in many skeletal formations. Lizards differ from the dinosaurs primarily in the formation of the skull, though there are other differences as well.

The 3,000 species of lizards that exist today represent a small number compared to the great diversity that existed in the past. However, lizards are found on every continent except Antarctica, although they do range as far south as Terra del Fuego, the southernmost tip of South America.

CLASSIFICATION

Snakes, lizards, and the burrowing tropical group called amphisbaenians are grouped together in the order squamata because they all possess paired reproductive organs, the hemipenes of the male, and hatchlings have an egg tooth on the snout.

Very few characteristics separate snakes from lizards. Through parallel evolution some lizards such as the glass lizards have lost their legs, probably adapting to their burrowing way of life. Most lizards however, have legs as well as external ear openings, small belly scales, and eyelids, which distinguish them from snakes.

Lizards are placed in the suborder lacertilia. Most saurians have legs but some, like the glass lizards, have only vestigial pectoral and pelvic girdles. The lower jaw, unlike the snakes, is united in front and is immovable. Unlike the snakes, most lizards have blunt, thick tongues (except for the monitor lizards) ear openings and eyelids. Most lizards chew or crunch up their food while the snakes swallow their prey whole. Also snakes suck up water while lizards usually lap it up with their tongues.

LOCOMOTION

With the exception of the glass and worm lizards, all Florida lizards have four legs. The glass lizards move using a modified serpentine motion, moving from side to side pushing with the sides of their bodies. They do not have the modified belly scutes found in the snakes. The worm lizard rarely crawls about on the surface of the soil. It spends most of its time in burrows. Its body scales resemble the rings of earthworms but it doesn't have the same "stretching-pulling" flexibility that earthworms have. Instead of the usual lateral snake-like undulations, worm lizards are capable of vertical movements.

Some lizards like the sand and mole skinks have short legs of equal size that are adapted for their fossorial life in sandy soils. The sand skink's legs and reduced-size toes are nearly vestigial and play little role in the burrowing habits of this species. The mole skinks spend more time above the surface, usually crawling about under cover of leaves, bark, and logs. Their legs are proportionately larger and more functional. The legs are used to pull the body along the ground. When the mole skink is trying to escape, the legs are pulled up to the body and the lizard uses snake-like movements instead of the legs. These burrowing species have smooth scales, a conical head, shovel-shaped snout, and cylindrical tail.

The remaining species of lizards have larger hind legs with longer, clawed toes that aid in running and climbing. Most geckos and anoles have special adhesive tissue pads that aid in climbing on surfaces, even on glass. These special tissues or lamellar surfaces are arranged in rows on the undersides of the toes.

When walking or running, most lizards move alternately on all four legs. However, to some degree, lizards like racerunners may utilize their hind legs in a bipedal gate. The tail is used as a counterbalance in running and climbing.

With the exception of sand and mole skinks, the skinks in Florida are to varying degrees arboreal or tree climbers. Most do not dwell in the canopy but cling to the tree trunks and lower limbs.

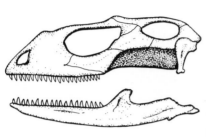

lizard skull

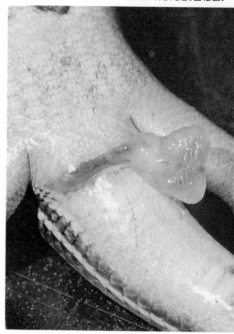

hemipenes of male broadhead skink

SENSES

Smell: Along with the sense of taste, the lizards have a well developed method of sensing chemicals. Most lizards flick their tongue, similar to snakes. They may touch the ground or objects with the tongue to pick up particles and return them to their mouth. The sense of smell is important to some species in detecting pheromones or minute chemicals released by other lizards. They may also use the sense of smell or taste to locate food.

Sight: Most lizards have a keen sense of vision. They are particularly attuned

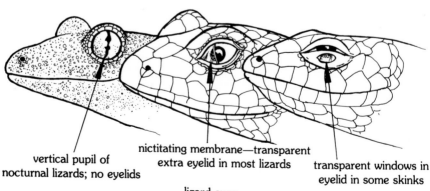

vertical pupil of
nocturnal lizards; no eyelids

nictitating membrane—transparent
extra eyelid in most lizards

transparent windows in
eyelid in some skinks

lizard eyes

to movement. Most do not have binocular vision and cannot accurately judge distances. Some lizards like geckos have vertical pupils as an adaptation for seeing in dim light. Diurnal lizards have round pupils. Some lizards have the ability to see colors while others see only black and white images.

Hearing: Unlike their close relatives, the snakes, lizards have an external ear opening and tympanic membrane. This indicates that they can pick up air vibration sounds rather well. Lizards are also quite sensitive to vibrations through the ground.

OBTAINING FOOD

With few exceptions, the lizards of Florida are insectivorous or at least feed on various forms of live arthropods including spiders and other invertebrates, including the eggs and pupa. The introduced green iguana and ctenosaur are notable exceptions—they graze on fruits and leaves and occasionally take insects.

Various species may have food preferences which may be based on food size compared to the size of the lizard or the time of activity of the lizard and prey. Some lizards like the geckos are active at night (nocturnal). Thus the food consists of nocturnal arthropods. Some lizards, racerunners and broadhead skinks, actively forage on the ground, stalking through leaf litter and around logs and stumps. Others, like the fence lizards, may hang upside down from a tree trunk watching for movement on the ground below.

Most lizards react to movement, and feed by sight, although hearing may play a role as well. When the prey is located, the lizard rapidly pounces on it, grabbing it in its jaws. The prey is crunched up in the mouth and is manipulated using the tongue and up and down motion of the jaws. Larger prey may be moved about or pulled using the claws and toes of the front foot. The tenderized prey is then swallowed whole.

Feeding occurs almost daily when the temperature and weather conditions permit. Feeding may take place at various times of the day, often immediately following a period of basking in the morning and again in the late afternoon during the summer.

BEHAVIOR AND REPRODUCTION

Most lizards are highly territorial and will defend at least a part of their home range, or the area where they feed, rest, mate, and bask. Rarely does the defense include mortal combat, but more often involves confrontation and display behavior. Display may consist of head bobbing, push-ups, and color display such as the dewlap in anoles, or flattening of the body to show belly colors in fence lizards. The intruding lizard usually scurries off to safety or assumes a submissive posture by lying flat to the surface or acting like a female. Occasionally when two closely matched males confront one another, and the intruder stands his ground, then a biting, rolling battle ensues. This rarely causes physical damage to either lizard beyond the possible loss of a tail or a few scars.

Anoles provide students with an excellent opportunity to study lizard behavior. They are relatively easy to capture and individuals can be marked for identification. Their movements can be plotted on a map of the habitat so that the home range can be determined. Behavior of individuals may be observed at length to determine times of various activities and the social rank of various individuals.

Similar studies can be conducted on captives if they are given adequate space and facilities. Territorial behavior should be considered when planning housing for lizards. Allow sufficient space if more than one male is to be kept in confinement.

Male lizards have a copulatory organ, the hemipenes, which remains inside the opening at the base of the tail until the sexual act. This organ consists of two hollow projections which are used only one at a time. Most lizards lay an average of 2 to 15 eggs each season. Where incubation of eggs outside the body would be difficult, some species are viviparous, giving birth to live young. Most lizards, like snakes, lay parchment-like eggs which are typically buried in rotting logs, sawdust piles, or warm sandy soils.

TURTLES

ORIGINS

The stock from which turtles have derived probably existed during the late Carboniferous some 350 million years ago since many turtle-like adaptations have been found in the fossil record of the early Triassic some 250 million years ago. These early turtles were armadillo-like with flexible but protective shells. By the time of the dinosaurs, turtles were developed nearly as they appear today. The long dermal plates expanded and fused to form the armored carapace. The ribs and backbone fused with this bony layer and the limb girdles were shifted under the shell and the bones became fused. By the Jurassic period some 181 million years ago, turtles could be recognized as such and many species were in existence. By this time, teeth had been replaced by a bony beak, and some could pull their head, tail and feet into the shell.

By the end of the Cretaceous, 130 million years ago, as the dinosaurs and many other forms of life became extinct, many of the modern genera of turtles began to appear such as *Trionyx,* the softshells. By the Pliocene, some 13 million years ago, most genera now found in Florida were present.

Today in many of the springs and fossil beds, the fossils of water turtles and giant land tortoises, larger than the present day Galapagos tortoises, can be found.

CLASSIFICATION

Turtles belong to the class reptilia but are not very closely related to the other groups of reptiles. All Florida turtles are in the suborder cryptodira, or those which can pull their heads directly into their shell. A more primitive group of turtles found in South America and Australia is the side-necked turtles or

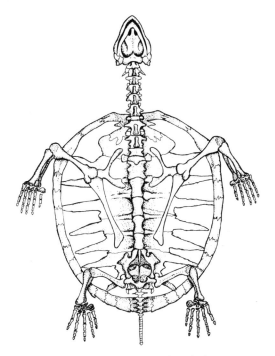

turtle skeleton—note fused ribs

pleurodira. These turtles must pull their head in sideways, folding the neck in an S-shape. Pulling the head directly into the shell requires specialized vertebrae and muscles which the more modern cryptodira have.

There are seven families of turtles represented in Florida.

LOCOMOTION

The old fable about the tortoise and the hare was basically correct. Turtles in general are rather slow on land: about the fastest sprint we have observed can be compared to a fast human walk. The only truly terrestrial turtles in Florida are the box turtle and the gopher tortoise. Their legs are adapted for carrying the heavy, bulky shell. The semi-aquatic *Pseudemys* or pond turtles have webs between their toes and the hind feet are paddle-like. These adaptations allow rapid movement in the water but do not inhibit terrestrial movements. On the other extreme, the softshells rarely leave water and the entire body and shell are streamlined for efficient movement underwater. The legs and feet are extremely webbed for excellent propulsion. The softshell can and does chase minnows on the swim.

On land or in water, turtles use alternating leg movements similar to lizards. The exceptions are sea turtles. Actually, when crawling on land even sea turtles use this gait; but in water, the strong front flippers are used in tandem to propel the turtle while the hind feet act as rudders.

Natural History   49

male courting female slider—note long claws

SENSES

Smell: It appears that the sense of smell is well developed in turtles. Apparently the pulsating throat causes air to move in and out of the mouth and nostrils, thus allowing odor causing particles to enter and be detected.

Turtles use this sense to find food and to locate other turtles. It may also aid in orientation as it does in so many other animals. Most turtles have scent glands somewhere on their body and the secretions most likely are involved with communication, particularly during courtship.

Sight: Turtles generally have eyes that do not focus together in binocular vision. This varies with each species, but the snapping turtle displays some binocular vision and thus is more accurate in judging the distance of its food. This may also be true of other predatory species such as the softshells. Generally eyesight in turtles is assumed to be similar to that of most lizards.

Touch: In addition to being very sensitive to vibration, the turtle's shell is also very perceptive to touch. Touch plays an important role in courtship in most turtles. Depending on the species, the male courts the female by chin rubbing, tapping on the shell, or in the sliders (*Pseudemys*) the male titilates the chin of the female or causes currents of water to move across the female in an attempt to excite her into mating. The sense of touch is also important in nest building and egg laying. The apparently cumbersome female manipulates and covers the eggs with rarely a cracked egg in the process.

OBTAINING FOOD

The types of food eaten by turtles are varied and each species has its preference. Check the species accounts for the diet of each. Turtles range from carnivores, like the softshells, to omnivores like most water and box turtles. while the gopher tortoise adults are almost entirely herbivorous. In many

50

species the young are carnivorous or insectivorous, but eat more plants as they grow older. Some turtles show specializations for feeding, e.g. the crushing plates and large heads of adult female map turtles which are adaptations for crushing the shells of snails and other mollusks.

The beaks of turtles provide a strong cutting edge which, used in conjunction with the front legs, allow the turtle to tear food into morsels small enough to swallow.

BEHAVIOR AND REPRODUCTION

Due to the passive behavior of certain species, turtles rival birds in their popularity as non-traditional pets. Turtles also have some ability to learn such things as associating the captor with food, thus begging that person for food. Results of studies on turtle intelligence have been mixed. Many researchers report that land turtles show greater intellect than their aquatic relatives. These conclusions may be due to the fact that aquatic turtles were studied on land, making their behavior less natural.

Very little is known about the social structure of turtles in the wild although there is some indication that some form of structure exists in tortoises, box turtles, and others. Anyone who has maintained a "herd" of turtles in captivity can begin to recognize dominant animals and the rank of others in the group. This is especially evident at feeding and breeding times. We know very little about how this affects behavior in wild populations.

We do know that land turtles, and to some degree aquatic turtles, live within a home range. Within this area, a turtle will have specific areas where it returns to

WILLIAM B. and KATHLEEN V. LOVE

box turtle hatching

feed, bask, and seek shelter. Also, some individuals may have overlapping home ranges. Most likely it is in these areas that social interaction takes place as it does with birds and other animals. There is some indication that turtles will defend some of their home range or what is commonly called a territory.

Herpetologists know much more about stereotyped behavior, that is, behavior that is practiced in virtually an identical manner by each individual of the same species. This type of behavior is most evident and most easily studied during courtship and breeding as well as during nesting. When courting, male turtles go through distinct and often very exact displays to entice a female into copulation.

Of all the reptile groups the turtles may show the greatest size difference between males and females, with the females often much larger than the males. Turtle and tortoise eggs may be hard shelled but more typically they have a soft rubbery consistency due to incomplete calcification of the whole shell. All turtles are oviparous, laying eggs in carefully constructed nests, often with intricate patterns of false nests to protect the main nest. Much research is being done on development of turtle eggs and on the ratio of male to female hatchlings. Incubation temperature seems to play an important roll in sex development.

CHECKLIST OF FLORIDA CROCODILIANS, LIZARDS AND TURTLES AND THEIR HABITATS

The following checklists are designed to give the reader an idea of the habitats that are used by each species of crocodilian, lizard, and turtle in Florida and their relative abundance (C = common, U = uncommon, R = rare) in that habitat. The "X" notation used in designating the habitat of the aquatic turtles in the river systems means that the turtle is found in that system, but it can be common or rare in different places on the river.

The charts should be used with the distribution maps, species accounts, and habitat descriptions. For example, by checking the map and account of the Florida worm lizard, you will see that this species is only found in central Florida counties and is restricted to very dry habitats.

One should note that just because a species is not listed in a particular habitat does not necessarily mean that it may not occur there, the reverse also being true. However, the listings are based on the most likely habitats used and the probability of locating the species in that habitat. The page number of the account is in parentheses after the species name.

AQUATIC TURTLES	Saltmarsh Mangrove	Escambia Perdido	Blackwater Appalachicola	Ochlockonee Econofina Fenholloway	Suwannee St. Marys	St. Johns	Withlacoochee Hillsborough	Manatee Myacca Peace	Kissimmee Everglades
Chicken									
Eastern (133)		X	X	X	X				
Florida (131)						X	X	X	X
Cooter									
Florida (124)		X	X	X	X				
Mobile (121)		X	X						
Peninsula (122)						X	X	X	X
Suwannee (118)	X			X	X				
Map									
Alabama (136)		X							
Barbour's (133)			X						
Mud									
Eastern (152)		X	X	X	X				
Florida (149)						X	X	X	X
Key (149)	X								
Striped (147)					X	X	X	X	X
Musk									
Loggerhead (152)				X	X	X			
Stripe-neck (154)		X	X						
Redbelly									
Alabama (126)	X	X	X						
Florida (124)	X			X	X	X	X	X	X
Snapping									
Alligator (114)		X	X	X	X				
Common (111)		X	X	X	X				
Florida (113)						X	X	X	X
Softshell									
Florida (160)		X	X	X	X	X	X	X	X
Gulf Coast Smooth (163)		X							
Gulf Coast Spiny (164)		X	X	X					
Spotted (129)				X	X				
Stinkpot (154)		X	X	X	X	X	X	X	X
Terrapin, Diamondback (138)									
Carolina (141)	X								
Florida East Coast (141)	X								
Mangrove (142)	X								
Mississippi (142)	X								
Ornate (142)	X								
Yellowbelly Slider (126)		X	X	X	X				
TOTAL NUMBER OF TAXA	9	14	13	13	13	9	8	8	8

	Pine Flatwoods	Sand Pine-Rosemary Scrub	Longleaf Pine-Turkey Oak	Xeric Oak Hammock	Mesic Hammock	Hydric Hammock	Tropical Hammock	Temperate Deciduous Forest
CROCODILIANS								
Alligator, American (60)								
Crocodile, American (64)								
LIZARDS								
Anole								
Brown (172)	U						C	
Florida Bark (174)								
Green (76)	C	C	C	U	U	C	C	U
Fence								
Florida Scrub (80)		C	U					
Southern (78)	C	C	C	C				U
Gecko, Reef (74)	U						C	
Glass Lizard								
Eastern (72)	C	R	U	R	U		U	U
Eastern Slender (68)	C	U	C	U	U			U
Island (70)	U	U	U	U				
Racerunner, Six-lined (99)		C	C	C				
Skink								
Broadhead (92)					C	U		U
Coal, Southern (82)	R					U		R
Five-lined (87)	C	U	C	C	C	U		C
Florida Sand (95)		U	U	U				
Ground (97)	C	C	C	C	C	C	C	C
Mole								
Bluetail (87)		U						
Cedar Key (87)				U				
Florida Keys (87)	U							
Northern (87)	U		U	U				
Peninsula (84)		U	U	U				
Southeastern Five-lined (90)	C	R	C	U	U	C	U	C
Worm Lizard, Florida (66)		U	U	U				
TERRESTRIAL TURTLES								
Box								
Eastern (147)	C		U		C			
Florida (142)	C	R	U		C			
Gulf Coast (144)	C							
Three-toed (147)	U		U		C		C	C
Tortoise, Gopher (157)	U	C	C	U				
SEA TURTLES								
Atlantic								
Green (103)								
Hawksbill (106)								
Leatherback (116)								
Loggerhead (101)								
Ridley (108)								

*Nesting

Terrestrial Habitats

Habitat abundance chart. Columns are habitat types; values are abundance codes (C = common, U = uncommon, R = rare; * as marked). Species/row labels appear on the facing page.

Farmlands, Fields and Disturbed Areas	Human Habitations, Golf Courses and Trash Piles	Coastal Beaches and Dunes	Salt Marsh	Mangrove Swamp	Freshwater Marsh	Temporary Ponds and Roadside Ditches	Permanent Ponds and Lakes	Cypress Swamps and Domes	Gum Swamps and River Swamps	Rivers	Small Streams and Creeks	Canals	Bays and Open Oceans
			U	U	C	C	C	U	C	C	U	C	R
			R	R			R						R
C	C	U											
C	C	R		U				U	U				
C	C												
C	C	U											
C	C	U											
C	U	U											
C	U	C				C							
U	U						U		U				
C	R						C		R				
C	C								U				
		R		R									
		R											
		R											
C	C												
R	R												
C	C												
C	C												
		U	U										
		R											
		R*		R									R
				R									R
		U*		U							R		R
				R									U R

Aquatic Habitats (bracket spanning Salt Marsh through Bays and Open Oceans)

55

CROCODILIANS, LIZARDS AND TURTLES

THE CROCODILES AND ALLIGATORS
ORDER CROCODILIA;
FAMILIES CROCODYLIDAE, ALLIGATORIDAE

There are approximately 22 species of crocodilians living today; most are considered threatened or endangered. Of these, there are two species of alligators, one in the United States, the other in China; five species of caimans, all in South America; and the long-snouted gavial (family gavialidae), of India. All the others are crocodiles which inhabit tropical areas throughout the world.

Crocodilians have bony, armor-like dorsal scales and soft, smooth belly scales. The belly plates are the ones used for making leather products. Hunting crocodilians for their hides, along with habitat destruction and persecution, may well end the 150 million year history of these great reptiles.

THE LIZARDS
ORDER SQUAMATA; SUBORDER LACERTILIA

Family Amphisbaenidae: the ringed lizards. The Florida worm lizard is not likely to be confused with other lizard groups but rather with the annelida, or earthworms. In all but one group, this family is distinguished by having no limbs, and a long worm-like body that is ringed with squarish scales. The eyes are concealed under the skin, and there are no ear openings. Most of the 140 species of this fossorial family live in the tropics.

All members of this family are burrowers and move through tunnels with little difficulty. On the surface, the worm lizard moves in a straight line, almost in a caterpillar-like fashion.

Family Anguidae: the alligator and glass lizards. This family, made up of 95 species, has a deep fold, or body groove, along the sides of the body from the neck to the beginning of the tail. The smooth scales lie flat against the body, are supported by bony plates, and feel hard to the touch.

Glass lizards have an extremely long tail but no legs. In most species, the tail will break easily due to fissures or weak areas in some of the tail vertebrae. The lost tail will be regrown in a short time. The glass lizard has eyelids and ear openings.

Family Gekkonidae: the geckos. Seven species of geckos are known to breed in Florida. Of this number, only one, the reef gecko, *Sphaerodactylus notatus* is believed to be native. As a group, geckos have large eyes, small scales, and round fleshy tails. Most have adhesive pads on the underside of their toes. Geckos are nocturnal animals, seeking shelter during the day. Most geckos have a distinctive call, something unique in the lizard world. The gecko family is primarily tropical and is made up of more than 650 species. All, except three New Zealand species, lay eggs.

Crocodilians, Lizards and Turtles

Family Iguanidae: the iguanids. The iguanids are the largest and most diverse family of lizards in the New World. The family includes a great variety of species from small anoles to large green iguanas and the unusual horned lizards. There are 650 species of iguanids, nearly all of which are found in the New World. The major characteristic of this family is the teeth, which fit into a groove on the side of the jawbone, whereas the other lizards have teeth that sit directly on the bone.

Most iguanids are egg layers and are active during the day.

Family Scincidae: the skinks. This family of about 550 species is found worldwide and is the most common group of lizards in some areas. The members of this family are generally characterized by having a cylindrical, smooth body. The legs are generally short, and the tail is long and round. Many of the Florida skinks are fossorial, that is, they burrow through sandy soils. *Neoseps,* the Florida sand skink, is fossorial and is endemic to Florida's high sandy areas.

While most members of this family bear live young, all the Florida species are egg layers. Most species are active during the day and are insectivores.

Family Teiidae: the racerunners. The teiids are a New World family of more than 225 species. Only one species of teiid is native to Florida, the race-runner; however, several Central American species have been reported as introduced in Dade county.

These lizards have large hind legs with large toes adapted for running over the ground. Most members of this family are semi-arboreal, diurnal carnivores or insectivores.

THE TURTLES
ORDER TESTUDINES

Family Cheloniidae: the marine turtles. This highly adapted group consists of four genera and six species, four species in Florida. They inhabit the warmer coastal waters of the United States. They are streamlined in design, and all four legs have developed into flippers. All of the marine turtles must return to their historic beach nesting sites to deposit their eggs, a behavior that may cause the extinction of this ancient group of reptiles. The combination of hunting by man (for eggs and adults), increased predation caused by an increase of natural predators such as raccoons, opossums, and dogs, and, most importantly, the destruction of the beaches caused by development, have taken their toll, and now all species are considered threatened or endangered.

One of the greatest wonders in the natural world has to be the way these "lowly" reptiles can navigate over thousands of miles of ocean and return year after year to the same "pin-point" islands to nest.

Family Chelydridae: the snapping turtles. This small family contains only three species, all of which occur in Florida. They are among the largest aquatic turtles, with the huge alligator snapper attaining a weight exceeding 200 pounds (90 kg). The head is extremely large, the tail long, and the cross-shaped plastron is greatly reduced. All species are pugnacious and exude a foul smelling musk when disturbed. Snapping turtles are relished for their fine tasting meat and are of economic importance in many parts of their range.

Crocodilians, Lizards and Turtles

Family Dermochelyidae: the leatherback sea turtles. Only one species, *Dermochelys coriacea,* the largest living turtle, represents this family today. The carapace lacks the scales of other turtles but is covered with a leathery hide which is saturated with oil. The large front feet and hind legs are flattened into flippers.

We know little about this rarely seen reptile. Observations of nesting in the United States are rare. Most nesting occurs on the shores of South America and the Caribbean Islands. There is a Pacific race that nests in the subtropical seas of the Australian region.

Family Emydidae: pond and marsh turtles. This is the largest family of living turtles, containing more than 80 species, 26 in the United States. The family is represented throughout the world with the exception of Australia. Most members of the family are aquatic or semi-aquatic, with some distinct exceptions like the box turtle. Both the plastron and the carapace are well developed and are covered with laminae.

Family Kinosternidae: the musk and mud turtles. This small family receives its common name from the foul smelling fluid that is released from under the carapace at the plastron bridge. The family is represented in the New World by 21 species, most of which occur in South and Central America. They are represented by eight species in the United States. These turtles are usually small and have oblong carapaces. The plastron in *Kinosternon* is hinged in two places, and is reduced in size in *Sternotherus.* They are bottom dwelling species, commonly observed walking on the bottom mud, rarely swimming about like many other aquatic turtles.

Family Testudinidae: the tortoises. This family consists of 39 living species of land dwelling tortoises. Representatives occur in North and South America, Europe, Africa, Asia, and some islands. Members of this group are usually medium to large in size, with the Galapagos Island tortoise being the largest living species of tortoise. The carapace and plastron are large and heavy. The hind feet are elephant-like. Only one genus, *Gopherus,* and three species occur in North America.

Family Trionychidae: the soft-shelled turtles. There are 22 living species of softshells that live in Africa, Asia, and North America. Four species occur in the United States, three in Florida.

All members of this family have a flattened, leathery carapace with an underlying bony shell in the center. The sides of the shell are flexible. The head, mounted on a long neck, is elongated with a long snorkle-like snout. The feet are broad and webbed for rapid maneuvering in water.

INTERPRETING THE SPECIES ACCOUNTS

For those not familiar with some terminology, it may be necessary to refer to the glossary and to the labeled illustrations in the back of the book.

The first italicized name listed at the top of each account is the scientific name. Scientific names are necessary to provide continuity. While a lizard or a turtle may have many common names, each is given one specific latinized scientific name. This name always belongs to only one species of animal. The first name is called the *genus*. Many animals have the same genus name. This means that they are all grouped together and are believed to be related. Each animal also has a second name called the *species*. Occasionally, a third latin name is given and is referred to as the *subspecies*.

If there are animals that are much alike but have only minor differences in color or form and are separated in their ranges, they may be given a subspecies name. They will all share a common genus name and species name, but the subspecies will be different.

Scientific Names	**Common Names**
Eumeces laticeps	broadhead skink
Eumeces egregius egregius	Florida keys mole skink
Eumeces egregius onocrepis	peninsula mole skink
Eumeces egregius similis	northern mole skink
Eumeces egregius lividus	bluetail mole skink
Eumeces egregius insularis	Cedar Key mole skink

These all share the genus *Eumeces*. The broadhead skink, *Eumeces laticeps*, has a different species name than the Florida keys, peninsula, northern, bluetail, and Cedar Key mole skinks, which share that same genus and species names, *Eumeces egregius*, but the subspecies names are all different, designating each as separate from the others. Note that some subspecies are important or different enough to warrant an entire account, while others are mentioned briefly within an account under the heading **Subspecies.** Any scientific name of three parts indicates that it represents a subspecies found in Florida and that other subspecies may be found in other areas. In some accounts the heading **Color Variants** is used. This is to indicate populations that vary considerably from the description given for the species. At one time many of these were considered subspecies.

A point of confusion may be the names listed between the scientific name and the common name. This is the name(s) of the person who first used that scientific name. For example: *Ophisaurus attenuatus longicaudus* McConkey **Eastern Slender Glass Lizard.** The author of this scientific name is McConkey. Sometimes the animal is moved to a genus other than the one in which it was originally classified. In this case, the name of the author of the original name is placed in parentheses. For example: *Deirochelys reticularia* (Latreille) **Chicken Turtle.** Latreille originally named this turtle. He called it *Testudo reticularia* in 1801. Since then this turtle has had at least seven different names. It was last called *Deirochelys reticularia* by Loding in 1922. Since its name is now different from the original given it by Latreille in 1801, his name is now placed in parentheses.

ABOUT THE MAPS

The county dots represent specimen records from that county. To be considered, specimens had to be preserved in a museum collection. Live specimens or preserved specimens in private collections were not considered because these are not usually available for study and the loss of them through time is more likely. Collections used in this survey included: The Florida State Museum, Carnegie Museum, U.S. Museum of Natural History, North Carolina State Museum, Tall Timbers Research Station, Florida Technological University, Auburn University, University of Michigan, American Museum of Natural History, California Academy of Science, Los Angeles County Museum, University of Kansas Museum of Natural History, Indiana University, Northwestern State University of Louisiana, University of Illinois, The Charleston Museum, and The Cleveland Museum. Locality data has been updated through 1980.

Counties without dots do not have specimens represented in the above collections. Dots with question marks indicate that the specimen and record is questionable.

Shaded areas approximate the range of the species, subspecies, or color variation. In all cases these are approximate and have never fully been determined.

Dots are centered in each county and do not represent exact localities. The decision to use the county dot method was based on the fact that most habitats are scattered islands in most cases and are not contiguous. Instead of trying to locate a specific locality, look for the proper habitat of a species within its range. A serious researcher will want to locate exact locality data available in the geographic files of research museums.

If a collector locates a specimen from a county not represented, he or she may want to notify a local museum or professional herpetologist in the above mentioned institutions. If the specimen has good accompanying data, it may be included in the collection.

SPECIES ACCOUNTS

Alligator mississippiensis (Daudin) **American Alligator**

Description: The maximum recorded length for this species is 19 feet (5.8 m), but animals only half that size are considered large today. The alligator has a broad shovel-like snout with the teeth set in jawbone sockets. The body and head are black with light banding on the sides and tail. The throat is white to creamy yellow.

Juveniles: Similar to adults but with distinct yellow or white banding.

Similar Species: The crocodile has a pointed snout and is gray, gray green or gray brown.

Natural History: The best known reptile in Florida, the alligator was once well on the way to extinction due to habitat destruction and market hunting for

The Crocodilians

adult American alligator

juvenile alligator

the hides. It is currently considered a threatened species in Florida. Laws protecting the alligator have allowed a remarkable recovery of this species. Today, the major threat to its existence is destruction of suitable habitat. A relatively docile species, the alligator can co-exist with man as long as it is left alone. People enjoy feeding alligators, but this causes them to associate man with food and to lose some of their fear of man, thus creating a potentially dangerous situation. Attacks by alligators are rare but serious injury and some deaths have occurred. The alligator begins life feeding on small aquatic invertebrates and other small animals. Fish, turtles, snakes, small mammals, and birds make up the diet of adults. Alligators are found in most bodies of water that are surrounded at least in part by marsh or swampy areas. They may move

The Crocodilians

for long distances during various stages of their lives but tend to stay within a home range as they grow older.

Some alligators may spend winters in dens dug into the side of banks or in marshes. The area around the den is usually deepened into a pond referred to as a "gator hole". Others may remain rather inactive during cold periods and come out to bask on warm sunny days.

Range of the American Alligator in Florida. Insert map shows general distribution of the species in the United States.

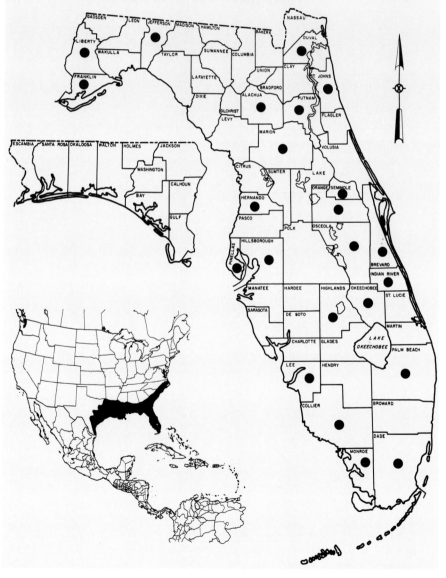

The Crocodilians

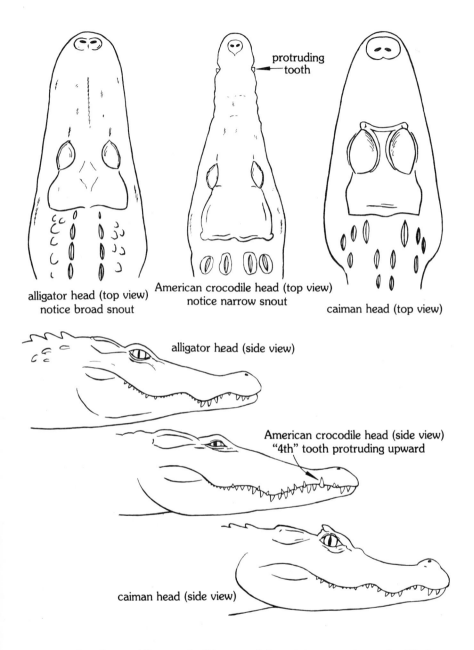

alligator head (top view)
notice broad snout

American crocodile head (top view)
notice narrow snout

protruding
tooth

caiman head (top view)

alligator head (side view)

American crocodile head (side view)
"4th" tooth protruding upward

caiman head (side view)

Reproduction: Alligators build nests of decaying vegetation and soil in late June or July. The nests, up to 3 feet high and several feet across, are built above the water line in marshes or on high ground near the water's edge. In the center of the nest, 30-50 two to three inch long, hard-shelled eggs are laid. The nests are attended by the female. Some will actually defend the nest and may be dangerous to humans at this time. The eggs hatch in approximately 70 days.

The Crocodilians

The young alligators stay together in a group or pod for at least the first year. During the winter, they remain with the female in the den. When alarmed, the small 'gators will croak. This call attracts the female, who may defend her young. Eggs and young alligators are eaten by many predators, especially raccoons and skunks.

DALE JACKSON

alligator nest

Crocodylus acutus (Cuvier) **American Crocodile**

Description: This giant reptile may reach a length of 15 feet (4.6 m). The long, pointed snout with the protruding teeth is the main characteristic of the crocodiles. The adults are gray to gray brown or gray green.

Juveniles: The young are gray brown, occasionally with rows of squarish dark brown blotches across the back and on the sides of the tail.

Similar Species: The alligator has a broad shovel-like snout and is black with faint bands of white or yellow present in younger individuals.

WILLIAM B. and KATHLEEN V. LOVE

American crocodile

The Crocodilians

Natural History: The crocodile is considered endangered and is protected by state and federal laws. Once occurring as far north as Palm Beach County, its range has diminished to the extreme southern part of the Everglades and the keys. Probably fewer than 500 individuals exist in Florida today. Other populations occur in Central America, the Antilles and northern South

Range of the American Crocodile in Florida. Insert map shows general distribution of the species in the United States, the Antilles, Central America, and South America.

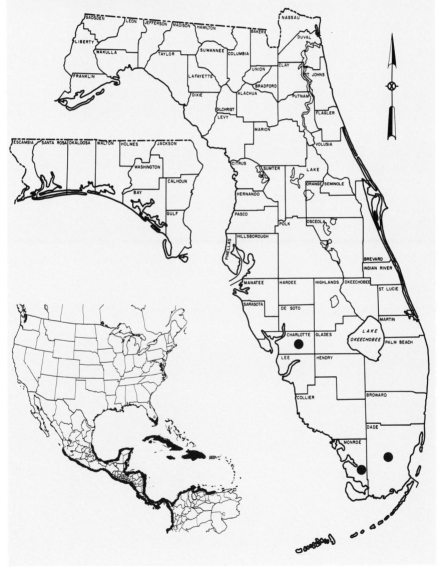

America. A major carnivore in the swamp habitat, the crocodile feeds on fish and other vertebrates. It is wise to avoid this animal and its nests.

The crocodile is normally found in brackish to salt water in coastal mangroves, brackish creeks, and may even be seen at sea.

Reproduction: The female lays 20-80 three inch eggs in a nest built in soil, marl, mud, or mat. The nest may be 5-20 feet in diameter or larger, and two or more feet high and may take a week or more to construct. The female attends the nest, which is built in late April or May, for more than 100 days of incubation. When the young hatch in late July or August, they make a croaking sound which attracts the female who may dig out the young. Some accounts state that the female will carry the young in her mouth to the water.

Rhineura floridana   (Baird)   **Florida Worm Lizard**

Description: This worm-like lizard reaches a length of 11 inches (28 cm). The scales are arranged in rings that make the body appear segmented. The squarish head is mimicked by the blunt tail. Eyes, ears and legs are lacking, and the mouth is recessed under the jaw. The body is pinkish to flesh colored, resembling a large earthworm.

Juveniles: Similar to adults.

Similar Species: The Florida worm lizard resembles a large earthworm but has a hard, bony head. It is reported that the worm-like two legged Arizona worm lizard (*Bipes*) has been released in Florida, but no specimens have been collected. The Arizona species has two mole-like front feet. The Brahminy blind snake, found in Dade county, has a rounded head and the tail has a slight tip.

Natural History: The worm lizard is found in dry upland hammocks, sand pine and longleaf pine-turkey oak habitats. It is not found in areas that may become saturated with water. The worm lizard is one of the few animals than cannot swim and avoids water. Like worms, they burrow through the soil. They apparently feed on small insects, possibly termites and ants. They are preyed upon by shrikes, and possibly worm-eating birds. Worm lizards are active

RAY E. ASHTON, JR.

Florida worm lizard

The Lizards—Amphisbaenids

during the fall—September and October—frequently coming above ground. Worm lizards are not lizards but amphisbaenids, which are a group of tropical burrowing reptiles. They will survive in captivity if given several inches of damp sand to burrow in and a constant supply of live termites.

Reproduction: Little is known about the reproduction of this animal. Two white oblong eggs are laid in late summer, probably underground. Eggs hatch in the late fall.

Range of the Florida Worm Lizard in Florida. Insert map shows general distribution of the species in the United States.

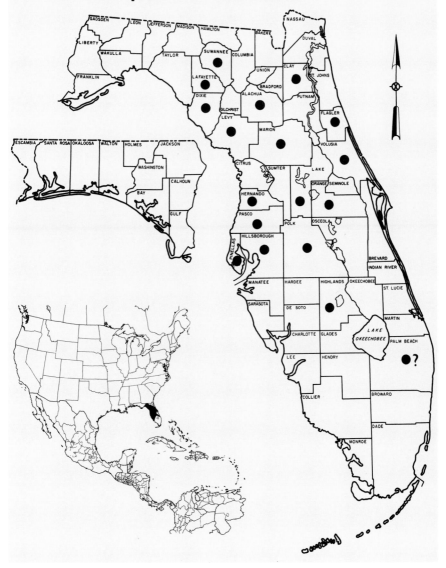

Ophisaurus attenuatus longicaudus   (McConkey)
Eastern Slender Glass Lizard

Description: Reaching a total length of 42 inches (107 cm), this lizard is tan to light brown. There is a dark mid-dorsal stripe down the back and several on the sides above and below the body groove. (See page 70.) Older individuals may have squarish light and dark blotches or crossbars on the sides and over the back.

Juveniles: Similar to young adults, they are tan with dark brown stripes.

Similar Species: Island glass lizards lack a stripe down the back or below the body groove. Sometimes it is very difficult to distinguish this species from other species of glass lizards. Adult eastern glass lizards are emerald green above and yellow below. Juvenile eastern's have a single dark stripe above the body groove.

Natural History: This species is commonly found in open, grassy or scrubby areas or in fallow fields. Where found, it is often very common. Like other glass lizards, they are burrowers that use sandy to sandy-loam soils. They are commonly found sharing the same habitat with one or both of the other species of glass lizards, particularly with the eastern glass lizard.

The slender glass lizard feeds on insects and spiders and lives within a home range of several hundred square yards. In captivity it will do well if given a warm, dry cage with sand to burrow in. It should be supplied with a diet of live insects. They will occasionally eat pieces of lean beef, chicken heart or chopped gizzard.

ZIG LESZCZYNSKI

eastern slender glass lizard

The Lizards—Anguids

Reproduction: Eggs are laid in midsummer in a nest under some cover or at the base of grass clumps. The 6-17 roundish white eggs are attended by the female. It is not likely that the female will defend the nest except possibly against very small predators.

Range of the Eastern Slender Glass Lizard in Florida. Insert map shows general distribution of the species in the United States.

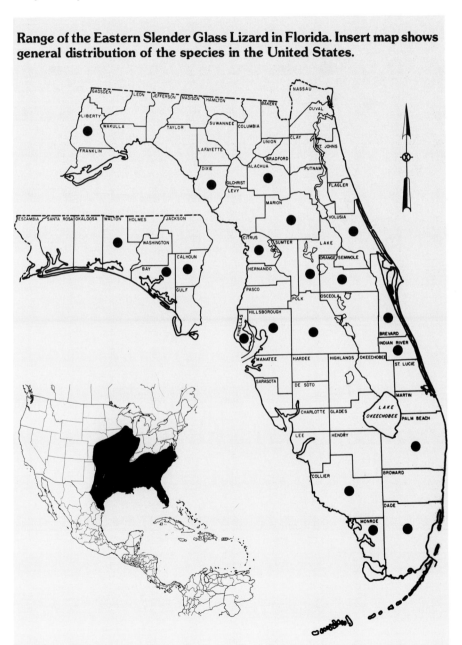

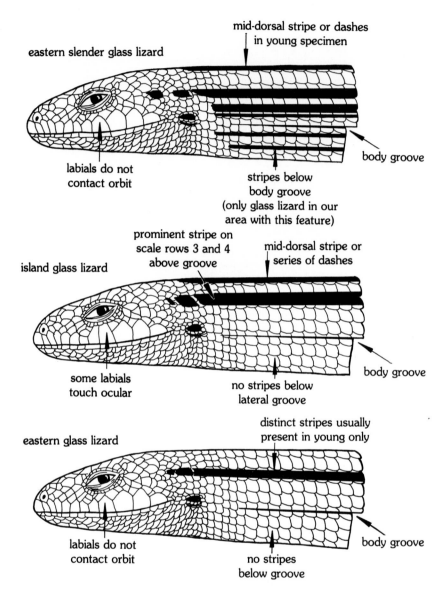

eastern slender glass lizard

mid-dorsal stripe or dashes in young specimen

body groove

labials do not contact orbit

stripes below body groove (only glass lizard in our area with this feature)

island glass lizard

prominent stripe on scale rows 3 and 4 above groove

mid-dorsal stripe or series of dashes

body groove

some labials touch ocular

no stripes below lateral groove

eastern glass lizard

distinct stripes usually present in young only

body groove

labials do not contact orbit

no stripes below groove

Ophisaurus compressus (Cope) **Island Glass Lizard**

Description: This species may reach a total length of 25 inches (64 cm). The body is generally tan to light brown. There is usually a single dark brown stripe on each side which lies above the body groove. Some individuals may have a very faint brown stripe down the center of the back. The underside is yellowish tan to pink without spots or stripes. The neck usually has a row of vertical white zigzag bars which extend along the sides to one-third of the body length. The snout is pointed. The eyelids and ear openings are present.

Juveniles: Similar to adults.

The Lizards—Anguids

Similar Species: The slender glass lizard has dark lines or spots below the body groove. The young eastern glass lizard has several stripes separated by narrow white lines on the sides.

Natural History: This hard to distinguish species is found primarily in old sand dunes along the coast of peninsular Florida. Inland, it is found in dry habitats such as sand pine scrub, longleaf pine-turkey oak, coastal hammocks,

Range of the Island Glass Lizard in Florida. Insert map shows general distribution of the species in the United States.

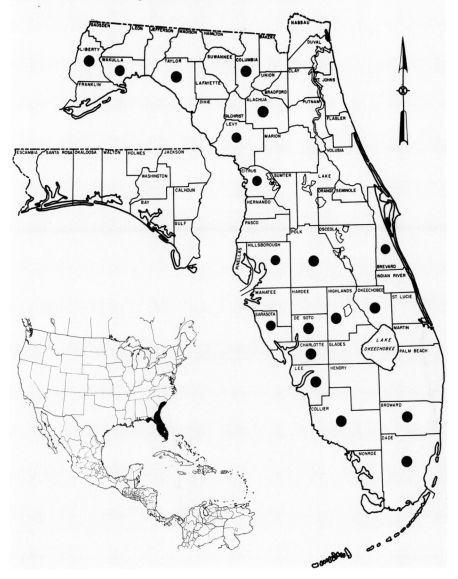

island glass lizard

and dry pine flatwoods. It is usually found under dead palmetto leaves or other debris. Occasionally this glass lizard will utilize gopher (*Geomys*) burrows and mounds. The primary diet of this species consists of insects, spiders, and other invertebrates. The tail of this rarely observed species does not break off as readily as do the tails of other species of glass lizards. It does well in captivity if given a dry cage with sand for burrowing and a diet of live crickets or grasshoppers.

Reproduction: Little is known about reproduction in this species. Like other glass lizards, it probably lays 7-10 roundish eggs which are attended by the female in an underground nest.

Ophisaurus ventralis   (Linnaeus)   **Eastern Glass Lizard**

Description: This beautiful lizard reaches a maximum length of 42.5 inches (108 cm). The dark stripes along the sides of the body are above the body groove. Usually there is no stripe down the center of the back; if one is present, it is faint. Young specimens are tan with dark brown stripes, resembling the slender glass lizard. Older adults are black with squarish emerald green spots covering the entire body. The underside is bright yellow. The scales are smooth and feel hard.

Juveniles: Similar to young adults.

Similar Species: The slender and island glass lizards have stripes down the center of the back. The slender glass lizard has stripes or spots below the body groove.

Natural History: The long tails of this and the slender glass lizard break off easily. Regrown tails may be a different color than that of the original tail and body. This glass lizard is common in open, moist, grassy areas. It is commonly found in grassy areas between canals and roadways and is often found on

The Lizards—Anguids

roadways during the early evening or midmorning. Glass lizards feed on insects, particularly crickets and grasshoppers. Glass lizards are semi-fossorial, that is, they burrow through loose, sandy soils.

When capturing this species, be sure to seize the body and not the tail. Further, do not allow the lizard to put pressure against the tail by twisting its body, or tail breakage will occur.

Range of the Eastern Glass Lizard in Florida. Insert map shows general distribution of the species in the United States.

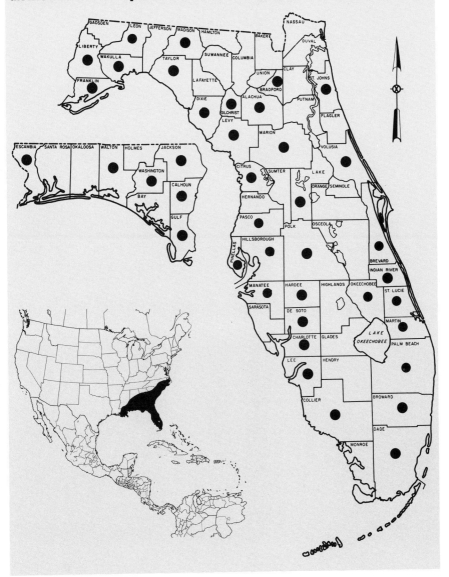

eastern glass lizard

After a brief period of acclimatization, this glass lizard will do well in a dry, warm terrarium with loose sand for burrowing and a diet of live insects. Older adults will eat young mice or chunks of lean meat.

Reproduction: Eggs are laid under or at the base of grass clumps. Up to 7-10 round, white eggs are laid and attended by the female. Eggs hatch in late summer, about 60-75 days after being laid.

Sphaerodactylus notatus notatus Baird **Reef Gecko**

Description: This tiny lizard may reach a length of 2 inches (51 mm), the smallest native Florida lizard. The head and body are brown. Females have two yellow stripes behind the head and are striped with brown, while males are faintly spotted. The tail is round and fleshy. The tips of the toes have small round adhesive discs. The scales are strongly keeled.

reef gecko

The Lizards—Gekkonids

Juveniles: The juveniles are marked like the females.

Similar Species: The ashy gecko and ocellated gecko are marked with light spots.

Natural History: This species is probably the only native Florida gecko. It inhabits vacant lots, trash piles and buildings, or may be found in some hammocks or on beaches. It feeds on small insects which it captures during early evening hours.

Range of the Reef Gecko in Florida. Insert map shows the general distribution of the species in the United States, Bahamas, and the Antilles.

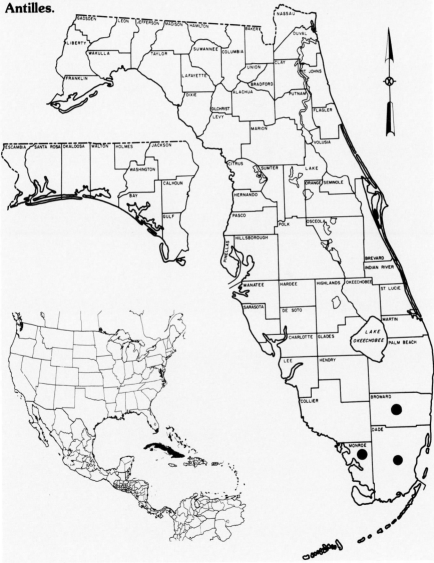

Reproduction: Single oval, white eggs are laid under cover, usually under debris or damp logs. When laid, the eggs are sticky and adhere to surfaces.

Anolis carolinensis carolinensis Voight **Green Anole**

Description: This medium sized lizard reaches a maximum length of 8 inches (20 cm). It has a slender body with fine, grain-like scales. The snout is long, pointed, and uniform in color. Males have a pink, red, or rarely green, throat fan (dewlap) and a slight ridge down the center of the back. The tail is long and slender and may break easily. The color of this lizard can change rapidly from bright green to brown, tan, or gray. The toes have adhesive pads on the undersides which allow the lizard to move on smooth surfaces.

Juveniles: The juveniles are similar to adults in shape and color.

ROBERT T. ZAPPALORTI

green anole

DAVID M. DENNIS

green anole—brown color change

The Lizards—Iguanids

Similar Species: The brown anole has a light stripe along the ridge down the center of the back and is often banded or spotted. The bark anole has a banded or ringed tail.

Natural History: The anole is often called a chameleon because of its ability to change color rapidly. Actually, the Old World chameleons are quite different in appearance and are only distantly related to the anole. The anole is

Range of the Green Anole in Florida. Insert map shows general distribution of the species in the United States.

The Lizards—Iguanids

probably the most obvious lizard in Florida. It inhabits nearly all types of habitat from dry woodlands to cypress swamps. It also does quite well around gardens and walks of buildings. It feeds on small insects and other invertebrates which it actively stalks. The males will extend their bright red dewlap and bob their heads in warning to trespassing males or to attract a nearby female. In some south Florida populations, the males have green dewlaps. With the use of their toe pads, anoles can climb in bushes and trees or even up the sides of buildings with great agility.

Anoles are diurnal, which means that they are active during the day. This, plus the fact that they are very common, makes them an excellent species to study. They are also easy to maintain in a dry terrarium which is occasionally sprinkled with water. They can be fed small, living insects such as crickets and mealworms.

Reproduction: Breeding takes place from early spring into the summer. One or two white leathery eggs are laid in damp soil in May or June. Hatching takes place in late summer. Juveniles mature in about eight months.

Sceloporus undulatus undulatus (Latreille)
Southern Fence Lizard, Fence Swift

Description: This medium sized lizard may reach a total length of 7 inches (18 cm). The rough scaled body is light to dark gray to almost black in some males. The females have zigzag bands across the back and tail. The males have a dark patch over the front shoulder. The throat and sides of the belly in the male are dark blue. The belly of the male is usually dark, while the belly of the female is usually buffy white with gray spots.

ROBERT T. ZAPPALORTI

southern fence lizard (fence swift)

The Lizards—Iguanids

Juveniles: Similar in appearance to adult females.

Similar Species: The scrub lizard has a dark stripe along the sides of the body.

Natural History: A very common lizard, particularly in pine flatwoods, xeric hamocks, and longleaf pine-turkey oak habitats. It is often found sitting on dead logs, trash piles, or the sides of trees, with its head downward looking for

Range of the Southern Fence Lizard in Florida. Insert map shows general distribution of the subspecies in the United States.

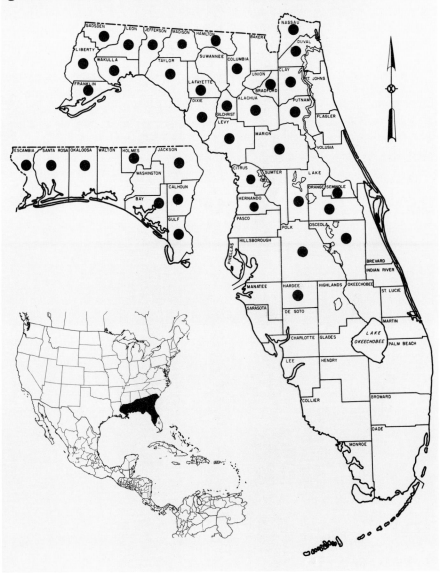

insects. Males are territorial and will bob their heads at other intruding males. If the intruding male approaches, the defender will turn sideways and display the blue belly patches. This is a very interesting and rather easy lizard to observe. Small beetles and other invertebrates are commonly eaten.

Reproduction: Breeding occurs in early spring. The eggs number 6-10 and are white, soft, and round. They are laid in a shallow nest at the base of grass clumps or in rotting wood. Sawdust piles are often used for nesting sites. A female may nest more than once a year. Hatchlings begin to appear in early June and may be found throughout the summer into early fall.

Sceloporus woodi Stejneger **Florida Scrub Lizard**

Description: This lizard, 5 inches (13 cm) long, is somewhat smaller than the fence swift. The scales on the body are rough and sharp. The back is gray to gray brown, particularly in males. Females have zigzag bars across the back. Both sexes have a dark brown stripe along each side of the body. Males have light blue on the throat and on each side of the belly. The bellies of females are white.

Juveniles: The young are similar to the adult females in appearance.

Similar Species: Southern fence lizards lack the dark side stripes. However, where the two species occur together, they may hybridize, making identification difficult.

RAY E. ASHTON, JR.

Florida scrub lizard

The Lizards—Iguanids

Natural History: This lizard almost exclusively inhabits fire maintained habitats such as pine scrub habitats, but may occasionally be found in longleaf pine and beach habitats that border scrub. When alarmed, it will take flight across open ground instead of climbing into the trees. Often it can be seen along dirt roadsides sitting head downward on pine trees watching for ants, beetles, crickets, grasshoppers and other insects. Males will bob their heads at intruding

Range of the Scrub Lizard in Florida. Insert map shows general distribution of the species in the United States.

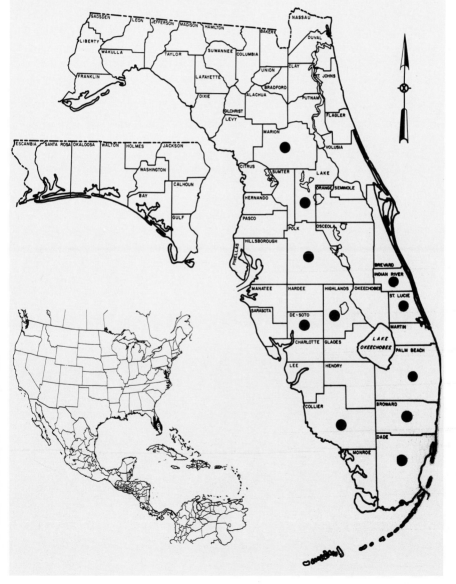

males or to attract females. Because of the tremendous loss of scrub habitat to orange groves and housing developments, this lizard's range has been greatly reduced.

Reproduction: Mating occurs from late March through June. Three or four weeks after mating, 2-4 round chalky white eggs are laid in the soil, such as in gopher (*Geomys*) and tortoise mounds, and hatch in about 75 days. The young mature in the first year.

Eumeces anthracinus pluvialis Cope **Southern Coal Skink**

Description: This rare lizard reaches a total length of 8 inches (20 cm). As in all skinks, the scales are smooth and shiny. There are four thin light stripes which extend from the head down the back and tail. The center of the back is tan or brown, and the sides are chocolate brown. There are two or more light spots on the jaw, behind the eye. The males have reddish jaws and cheeks during the breeding season.

Juveniles: The young have a completely black body with faint light stripes. They may also have red on their lips and a bright blue tail.

Similar Species: Both species of five-lined skinks and female and juvenile broadhead skinks have five lines along their sides and back. They also have a V-shaped pattern on the top of the head which is lacking in the coal skink.

Natural History: A very rare lizard in Florida, the coal skink inhabits moist hillsides of deciduous woodlands and pine flatwoods in the western panhandle of Florida. They are found under rocks or logs, often close to water.

JOSEPH T. COLLINS

southern coal skink

The Lizards—Scincids

They will even dive into the water to escape a would-be pursuer. The coal skink feeds on small insects it finds while foraging through leaf litter. Little is known about the habits of the species in Florida. The authors collected one specimen.

Reproduction: Nesting probably occurs in midspring. Females lay 9-11 eggs in a nest which is usually under rocks. The female attends the eggs in a manner similar to the five-lined skinks. Hatching occurs in 1-2 months.

Range of the Coal Skink in Florida. Insert map shows general distribution of the species in the United States.

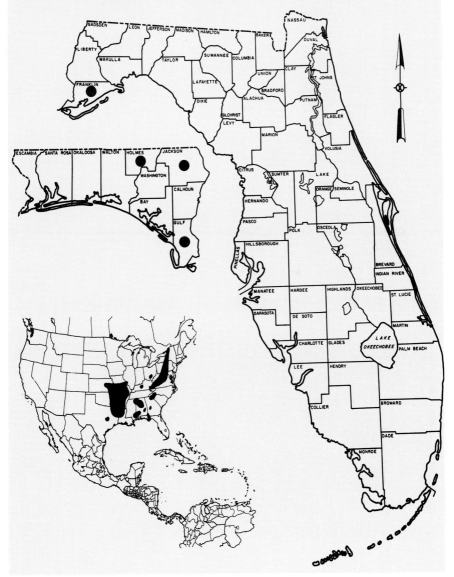

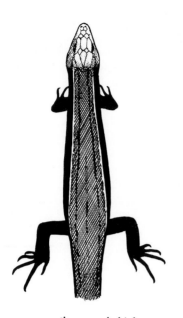

southern coal skink   five-lined skinks and broadhead skink

Eumeces egregius onocrepis (Cope) **Peninsula Mole Skink**

Description: This small slender lizard may reach a total length of 6 inches (15 cm). The scales are smooth and shiny. The body is long and cylindrical with tiny legs and five small toes on each foot. The body is light to dark brown with a distinguishing yellow stripe extending from the nose, over each eye and onto each side. The tail is pink to red, or light blue. The upper jaw has a row of squarish spots.

RAY E. ASHTON, JR.

peninsula mole skink

84

Range of the Peninsula Mole Skink in Florida is designated by the open area, Bluetail Mole Skink by the ⫽⫽ area, Florida Keys Mole Skink by the ⫶⫶⫶ area, Northern Mole Skink by the ⫶⫶⫶ area, Cedar Key Mole Skink by the ▦ area. Insert map shows general distribution of the species in the United States.

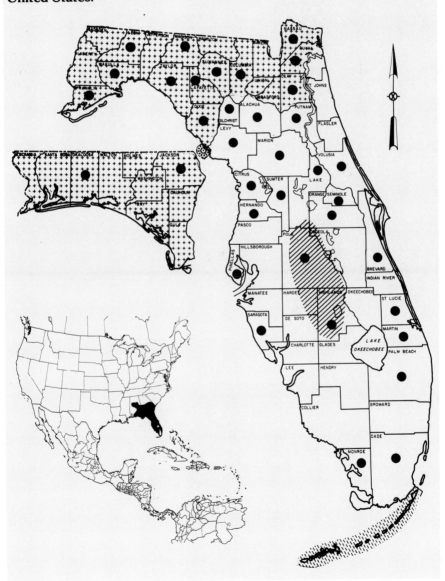

northern mole skink

bluetail mole skink

Natural History: A very secretive but apparently gregarious lizard, it is rarely seen but is not necessarily rare where it occurs. Mole skinks inhabit xeric hammocks, sand pine scrub, and longleaf pine-turkey oak. Occasionally they may be seen scurrying about through the sparse leaf litter or around dead palmetto fronds. During warm days or near the end of winter, they may be found just under the surface of pocket gopher or burrowing beetle mounds. When alarmed, they virtually dive under the sand. They may utilize the gopher (*Geomys*) burrows regularly. They feed on small insects and other arthropods.

Reproduction: After breeding, females may remain inactive, almost as if in hibernation. Mating occurs in the fall, winter or early spring. Nesting occurs from April through June. The 2-4 elliptical white eggs are laid in a nest cavity

　　　　　　　　　　　　　　　　　　　The Lizards—Scincids

Florida Keys mole skink

excavated by the female. The cavity may be six feet under the soil surface. The eggs are attended by the female until hatching occurs in 31-51 days.

Subspecies:

Eumeces egregius egregius Baird **Florida Keys Mole Skink** The dark brown body has eight yellow stripes which may extend to the tail base. The tail is red to brownish red with thin black stripes. It has seven upper labials and 22 or more scales around the midbody.

Eumeces egregius similis McConky **Northern Mole Skink** The body is gray to tan and the tail is red orange or reddish brown. It has six upper labials and 21 or less midbody scales.

Eumeces egregius insularis Mount **Cedar Key Mole Skink** The eight stripes found in other subspecies are inconspicuous or lacking. In some specimens there is a pair of dorsal lateral light stripes running the length of the body. The tail is dark orange, and it has 21 or less midbody scales. The young are a uniform black color.

Eumeces egregius lividus Mount **Bluetail Mole Skink** The tail is light blue in young skinks and is light blue to salmon pink in the adult. The body stripes widen as they extend onto the back. Seven upper labials are present on each side. This subspecies is considered threatened due to development of its highland habitat.

Eumeces fasciatus (Linnaeus) **Five-lined Skink**

Description: This medium sized skink may reach a total length of 8 inches (20 cm). The females are dark brown with five light stripes down the back. The males may or may not have faint stripes on the back but usually the center of the back is light brown with darker sides. The underside of the tail has a central row of wide scales. During the spring mating season, the males have orange-red jaws and cheeks.

The Lizards—Scincids

R. W. VAN DEVENDER

male five-lined skink

RAY E. ASHTON, JR.

female five-lined skink

Juveniles: The young are very dark brown to black with five white stripes down the back, and have a bright blue tail.

Similar Species: The underside of the tail in the southeastern five-lined skink has scales of uniform size. Male broadhead skinks are uniformly brown without stripes; females are very difficult to distinguish.

Natural History: A very uncommon species in Florida; most five-lined skinks observed are the southeastern species (*E. inexpectatus*). When located, it may be found in large numbers. It inhabits stumps, rotting logs, abandoned houses, and trash piles, around hydric hammocks. It feeds on a large variety of invertebrates. The bright blue tail of the juveniles may be used to divert attacks of predators to it instead of to the body or head. When grabbed, the tail breaks off and thrashes about wildly. A new tail will soon be regenerated in its place.

The Lizards—Scincids

Reproduction: Mating occurs in April and early May. The female then nests under cover or may dig out a nest site in the ground. Four to 15 ovoid, soft white eggs are laid in the nest. The female then coils around them until they hatch. She may defend them from small predators and will maintain the nest to insure proper humidity. If the egg chamber gets too dry, she will void fluid from her bladder over the eggs. Eggs hatch in about two months.

Range of the Five-lined Skink in Florida. Insert map shows general distribution of the species in the United States.

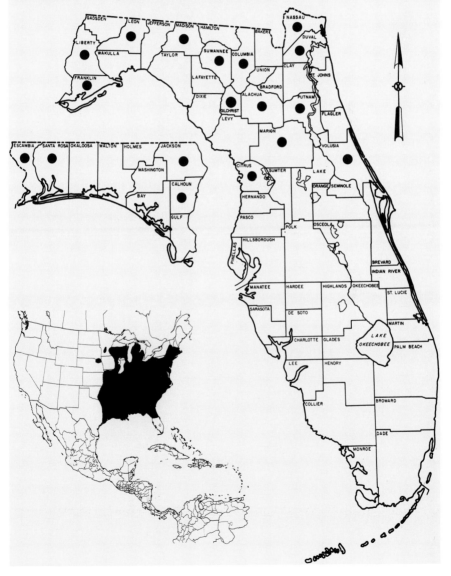

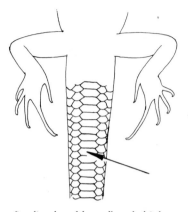
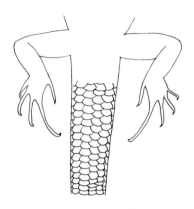

five-lined and broadhead skinks
center row of enlarged scales
on underside of tail

southeastern five-lined skink
scales on underside of tail
are all similar

Eumeces inexpectatus   Taylor
Southeastern Five-lined Skink

Description: This shiny-scaled skink may reach a length of 8 inches (21 cm). The females are dark brown with five yellow-white stripes down the back. In males, these stripes may be much fainter, and the back may be a light brown. The tail may be brown to bluish in adults. The scales along the underside of the tail are all about the same size. During the spring breeding season, the males have orange-red jaws and cheeks.

DAVID M. DENNIS

male southeastern five-lined skink

The Lizards—Scincids

Juveniles: The young are black with five narrow white stripes and a bright blue tail.

Similar Species: Five-lined skinks and broadhead skinks have a row of large scales along the underside of the tail. Females and juveniles of all three species are very difficult to distinguish.

Range of the Southeastern Five-lined Skink in Florida. Insert map shows general distribution of the species in the United States.

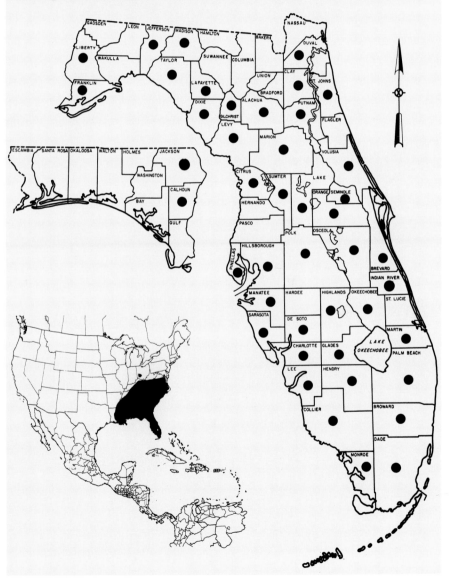

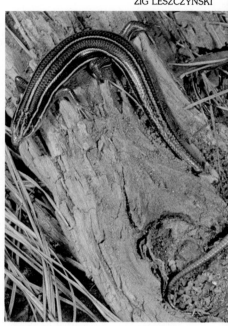

juvenile southeastern five-lined skink   female southeastern five-lined skink

Natural History: One of the most common lizards in Florida, the southeastern five-lined skink inhabits drier habitats, but may be found in and around wetter pine flatwoods and cypress heads. They are commonly found around abandoned buildings, log piles, rotten logs, and stumps. This species doesn't appear to be as arboreal as the broadhead skink. It feeds on small insects and other arthropods it finds while scratching through the ground cover. When alarmed, it will disappear into leaves or under logs, or may even take to the water. During the winter it can be found coiled in the damp center of rotting stumps.

Reproduction: Six to eight ovoid, soft, white eggs are laid in a nest cavity dug by the female in the late spring. The nest may be in a rotting log or in the ground under cover. While incubating, the eggs are attended by the female. Apparently the female will defend and care for the eggs as does the five-lined skink. Hatching takes place in midsummer.

Eumeces laticeps (Schneider) **Broadhead Skink**

Description: This largest of the five-lined skinks and one of the largest native lizards in Florida may reach a length of 13 inches (32 cm). The males are brown or dark tan with thick, broad-jowled heads. During the spring, the heads of the males are orange to bright red. Females are brown with two yellow stripes on the sides of the body and a faint yellowish-tan stripe down the center of the back. The underside of the tail has a row of large scales.

Juveniles: The young are black with five narrow, yellow-white stripes and a bright blue tail.

Similar Species: Southeastern five-lined skinks lack the row of large scales under the tail. Five-lined skinks have four small scales touching the front of the ear opening; the broadhead skink has only two.

Range of the Broadhead Skink in Florida. Insert map shows general distribution of the species in the United States.

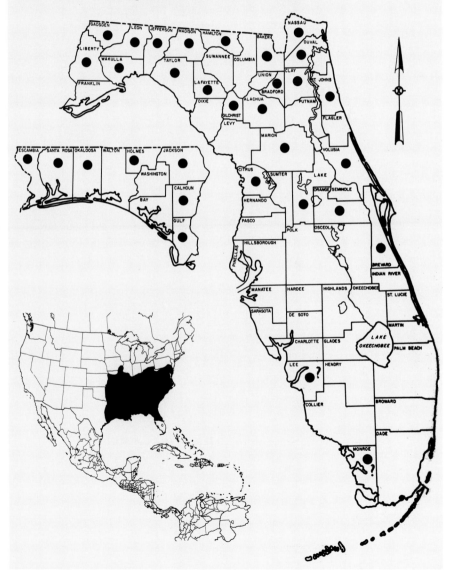

female broadhead skink with eggs

Natural History: Broadhead skinks are most commonly found in mesic hammocks, around cypress heads or other damp environments, or at the edge of xeric hammocks. They are seen sitting in the sun on the tops of dead logs or stumps. When alarmed, the broadhead skink will run up into the trees.

They feed primarily on beetles and beetle larvae. The authors have often shared their lunch with these lizards. A piece of bread, meat, or banana tossed within a few feet of an individual will cause it to begin tongue touching and movement in a back and forth search pattern until the tidbit is located, apparently by smell.

Males can inflict a painful bite and should be handled with respect. As in other skinks, the tail breaks off easily in this species.

The broadhead skink hibernates during cold spells under the bark or in the moist inner portion of rotting stumps.

Reproduction: Mating occurs in April and May, during which time males do furious battle with each other. Females are grabbed unceremoniously by the neck by the males during copulation. Eight to 11 ovoid, soft, white eggs are laid in a nest in a rotting log or sawdust pile. The author has observed a nest with the female coiled around the eggs. Whether she defends the eggs or not is unknown.

broadhead skink—5 labials

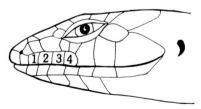

five-lined skink—4 labials

The Lizards—Scincids

juvenile broadhead skink

male broadhead skink

Neoseps reynoldsi Stejneger **Florida Sand Skink**

Description: This cylindrical, smooth-scaled skink may reach a total length of 5 inches (13 cm). The legs are very tiny and have only one toe on the front and two toes on the hind feet. The overall color is silvery gray or white to tan. The eyes are tiny, and the lower eyelid has a clear window. There are no ear openings.

The Lizards—Scincids

Juveniles: Similar to adults.

Similar Species: Mole skinks have small ear openings, five toes on each foot, and light lines are present over the eyes and extend onto the back.

Natural History: A secretive skink, it spends most of its time underground, sliding through sand with little effort. They are found in xeric habitats like upland sandhills, sand pine scrub and adjoining turkey oak habitats.

Range of the Florida Sand Skink in Florida. Insert map shows general distribution of the species in the United States.

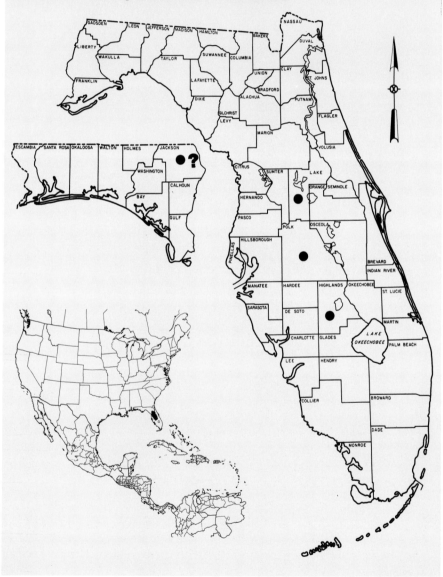

The Lizards—Scincids

Florida sand skink

Occasionally, the sand skink is found under objects such as dead palmetto fronds. Sometimes they are collected by raking through the loose sand of pocket gopher mounds, particularly on sunny days during late winter and early spring. They feed on termites, ants, and insect larvae. Little is known about the natural history of this species. The Florida sand skink is considered threatened due to development and agriculture in its upland habitat.

Reproduction: Mating occurs in March and April. Probably two eggs are laid about two months after mating. Eggs are probably laid in underground nests. Hatching occurs in July.

Scincella laterale (Say) **Ground Skink**

Description: This tiny lizard, 5 inches (13 cm) long, has a small head and a body that is long and round. The legs are very small. The center of the back and lower sides are light brown. There is a wide dark stripe along the upper sides. The belly is bluish gray, with a yellowish or green color down the center. The lower eyelid has a clear window. The tail is brown to bluish black.

Juveniles: Similar to adults in shape and coloration, but the tail may be bluish gray in the juveniles.

Similar Species: Mole skinks have a light stripe over each eye and down the back. The sand skink is light gray and has only one or two toes on each foot.

Natural History: A very common lizard, the ground skink is found in almost all habitats that have some ground cover such as grass or dead leaves. They are commonly seen in lawns. When alarmed, the skink moves in a snake-like manner in the leaf litter. They will also take to the water to escape. Once under the litter or water the skink is very difficult to find again. Ground skinks feed mainly on small insects, millipedes, and other invertebrates. They may occasionally take a bite out of their own tail, mistaking it for some wiggling prey. Ground skinks are relished by many species of snakes, especially young king-

The Lizards—Scincids

snakes, coral snakes, and scarlet snakes. Easily obtainable all year round, they make an excellent food source for captive snakes.

Reproduction: Mating takes place in late winter to early spring. Eggs can be deposited throughout the warmer months. Two or three small, white, thin-shelled eggs are laid in moist humus, logs, or rotting vegetation. Eggs hatch in about two months. This species is capable of breeding within its first year.

Range of the Ground Skink in Florida. Insert map shows general distribution of the species in the United States.

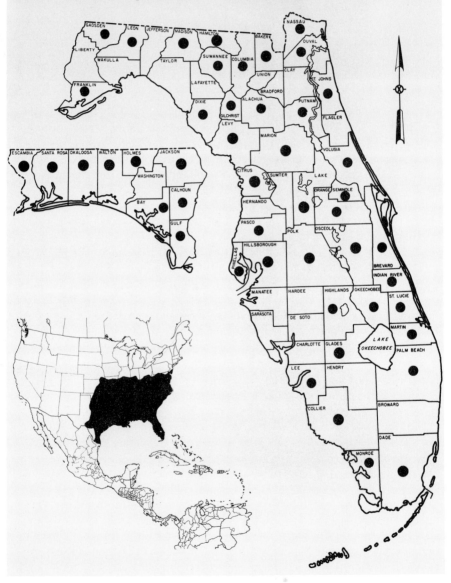

The Lizards—Scincids

ground skink

Cnemidophorus sexlineatus sexlineatus (Linnaeus)
Six-lined Racerunner

Description: This common lizard may reach a total length of 9.5 inches (24 cm). It has a wedge-shaped pointed snout. The upper part of the body is covered with tiny scales, and the underside (belly) is covered with large squarish plates. The head and body are brown with six yellow to tan stripes down the back. The hind legs are much larger that the front legs, and the fourth toe on the hind foot is very long. Males have a bluish throat and belly.

six-lined racerunner

The Lizards—Teiids

Juveniles: Similar to adults but with a light blue tail.

Similar Species: Skinks have shiny scales on their back and their front and hind legs are nearly the same size.

Natural History: This lizard is very common in dry habitats where there are open ground and sandy areas, including beach dunes. This swift lizard is most active during the heat of the day. It can often be heard as it thrashes about

Range of the Six-lined Racerunner in Florida. Insert map shows general distribution of the species in the United States.

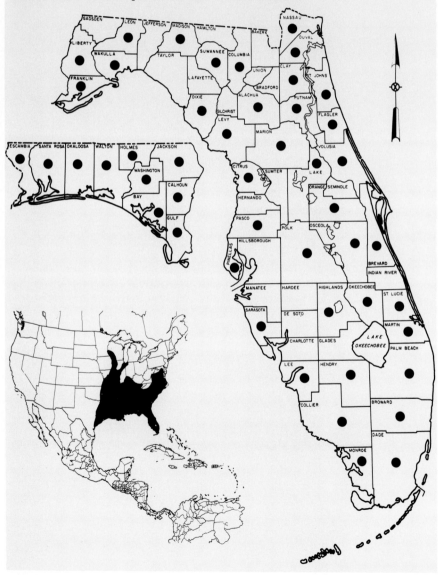

The Lizards—Teiids

in dry leaves in search of insects. During the night and during cold periods, the racerunner retires to an underground burrow which it has dug or to an abandoned burrow of some other animal like a burrowing beetle or wolf spider. The racerunner is eaten by coachwhips, racers, and probably by other species of lizard eating snakes as well as by hawks and shrikes.

Reproduction: Mating occurs in early spring. The male goes through an interesting courtship pattern. He begins by rubbing his cloaca on the ground while crawling in a figure eight. He nips at the neck of the potential mate while rubbing the female's back with the underside of the hind legs. If the female accepts him, he coils his tail under the female while biting onto the back, and copulation takes place.

From four to six eggs are laid under a log, bark, or other cover late in the spring. The eggs are white and oval in shape and hatch in about two months.

Caretta caretta caretta (Linnaeus) **Atlantic Loggerhead**

Description: This turtle has a large elongated reddish-brown carapace and may attain a length of 48 inches (122 cm) and a weight of up to 200 pounds (91 kg). There are five costal scales on each side of the carapace, the first one touching the nuchal scale; there are three or four scales on the bridge between the carapace and plastron. (See page 109.) There may be light colored skin surrounding the head scales. The large head and blunt jaws characterize this species. The plastron is yellow and the flippers are reddish brown.

PETER C. H. PRITCHARD

Atlantic loggerhead

Juveniles: The hatchlings are brown above, yellowish to tan below. The carapace has three keels, and the plastron has two.

Similar Species: The ridley has a roundish shell, is olive green in color, and the bridge has four large scales. The hawksbill and green turtles do not have the costal scale touching the nuchal.

Range of the Atlantic Loggerhead is in the warm waters of the Atlantic Ocean and Gulf of Mexico and the Caribbean, north to Canada and south to Argentina.

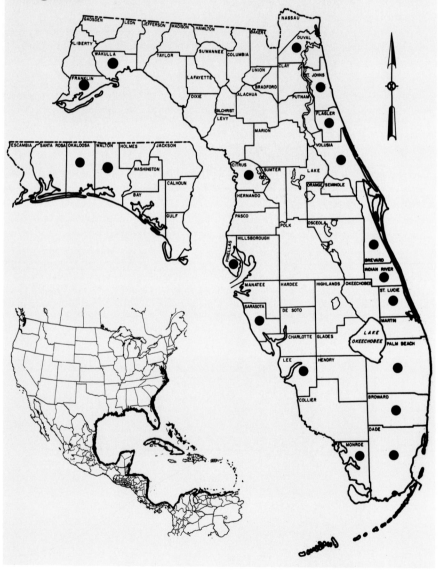

The Turtles—Cheloniids

juvenile Atlantic loggerhead

Natural History: The loggerhead travels far and wide over open oceans and is found in bays and estuaries along the coasts. Little is known about their behavior and movements beyond the nesting beaches.

Loggerheads are omnivorous, feeding on various mollusks, sponges, and other marine invertebrates as well as on turtle grass and algae. Life expectancy is at least 20 years.

Like all other sea turtles, the loggerhead is hunted for its meat, especially on Caribbean islands. The nests are also raided for the eggs. Due to destruction of nesting beaches, continued heavy collecting pressures, and persecution by fishermen, this species is in great jeopardy and is considered threatened.

The most important U.S. nesting beaches for this species lie between Cape Canaveral and Palm Beach.

Reproduction: Females come ashore from April to August at high tide to select a nesting place above the high tide level. The funnel-shaped nest is dug using the hind flippers. Fifty to more than 100 eggs are laid, and all hatch at nearly the same time in 60-100 days. The hatchlings dig themselves out of the nest and move rapidly to the water.

Chelonia mydas mydas (Linnaeus) **Atlantic Green Turtle**

Description: This medium to large size turtle has a shell length of 60 inches (153 cm) and weighs 250-280 pounds (113-127 kg). The front legs are large and paddle shaped. The general color is brown to olive brown. The carapace may be light brown with mottlings or blotches of dark brown; the scales on the carapace do not overlap. The scales on the head are bordered by yellowish skin. There are four costal plates on each side of the carapace, the first of which does not touch the nuchal scale, and there is one pair of prefrontal scales.

The Turtles—Cheloniids 103

Atlantic green turtle

Juveniles: The carapace is dark brown or black, and the plastron is nearly white. The tips of the flippers are black.

Similar Species: The loggerhead and ridley have nuchal scales which touch the first costals. The hawksbill has overlapping scales on the carapace and four prefrontals.

Natural History: The green turtle migrates across open seas for long distances to feeding, breeding, and nesting grounds. One of the great mysteries

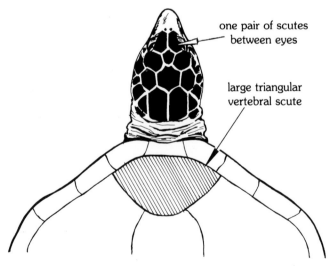

head and anterior carapace of Atlantic green turtle

The Turtles—Cheloniids

in the natural world is how these and other species of sea turtles navigate the high seas and locate their ancestral nesting beaches.

Adults graze on turtle grass and will occasionally eat crabs, jellyfish, and other marine invertebrates. Juveniles feed mostly on invertebrates. Green turtles feed during the day; at night they sleep under marine ledges or other protected areas.

Range of the Atlantic Green Turtle is in the warmer waters of the Atlantic, the Gulf of Mexico, and the Caribbean, occasionally as far north as Massachusetts and south to Argentina.

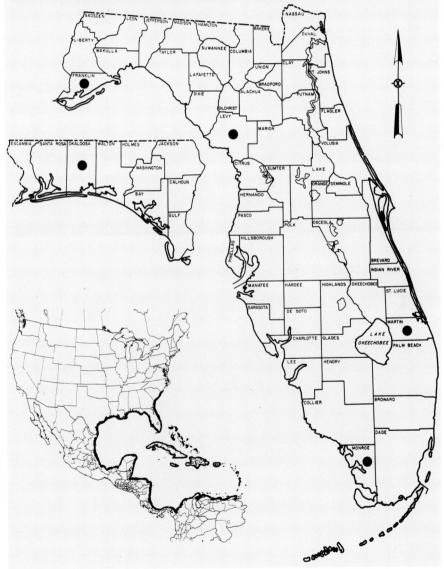

Like all other sea turtles, the green turtle has been greatly reduced in numbers due to hunting pressure on the adults and the raiding of nests for eggs. This species is considered endangered in Florida.

Reproduction: Mating occurs off nesting beaches. Females come ashore to nest on sandy beaches from May through June, and may nest several times each season. After finding an appropriate nesting site, the turtle digs out a body pit with the front flippers and then, using the hind feet, an egg chamber. A hundred or more spherical eggs are laid. Eggs hatch in about 45-60 days. All the hatchlings work together at digging to the surface, then they scurry to the water. Little is known about their behavior until they return as adults to the nesting beach. Although, at one time, nesting may have occurred on many Florida beaches, the only major nesting area remaining occurs·between Cape Canaveral and Palm Beach.

Eretmochelys imbricata imbricata Linnaeus
Atlantic Hawksbill

Description: One of the small sea turtles, the hawksbill may reach 36 inches (91 cm) in length and weigh 100 pounds (45 kg). The carapace is heart shaped and has a keel down the center. The scales on the carapace overlap except in very young and old animals. The general color is brown with a yellow, brown or black "tortoise shell" or radiated pattern. There are four scales between the eyes. Yellow skin shows between the head scales. The upper jaw has an enlarged hawk-like beak.

ROBERT S. SIMMONS

Atlantic hawksbill

The Turtles—Cheloniids

Juveniles: The carapace and head are black or dark brown. The edge of the carapace is yellowish, as is the plastron.

Similar Species: Green turtles have only one pair of prefrontal scales between the eyes.

Natural History: A very aggressive turtle, the hawksbill will bite and scratch with great vigor when first captured. Very little is known about the behavior of this turtle. The young hawksbills virtually disappear for several

Range of the Atlantic Hawksbill in Florida is in the warmer Atlantic waters, into the Gulf of Mexico and Caribbean Sea.

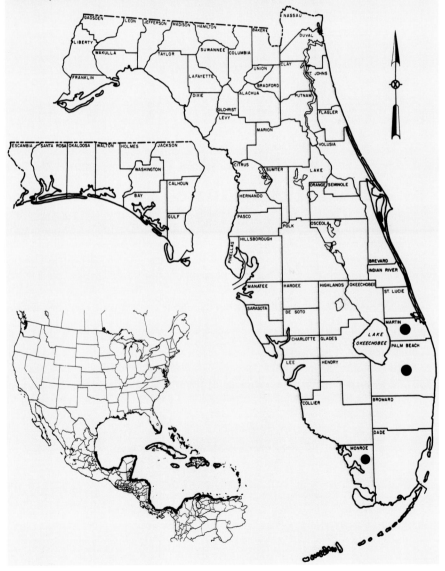

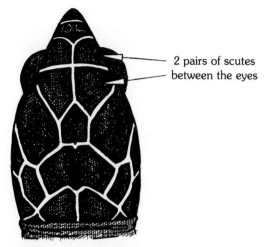

2 pairs of scutes
between the eyes

Atlantic hawksbill head

years after leaving the nest. Small turtles, 6 inches (15 cm) to adults are found around coral reefs.

Hawksbills feed on marine invertebrates, including jellyfish, sponges, crabs, and various mollusks. They also feed on marine algae and mangroves. They are seen most often around coral reefs.

Hawksbills are taken for their meat and for their shell, which has been used in the fashion industry to make tortoise shell jewelry for many years. Eggs are also collected from nesting beaches. The hawksbill is considered endangered throughout its range.

Reproduction: Females nest on sandy beaches throughout the Caribbean. The female comes ashore at night and crawls in a fashion similar to land turtles. She clears the nesting site with her fore flippers; then the cavity is dug with the hind feet. About 160 spherical, white, soft-shelled eggs are laid in the nest, which is then covered. The turtle pushes sand back over the nest with the hind legs.

Hatching takes place in about two months, with hatchlings usually emerging at night or in the evening. All of the eggs hatch at nearly the same time, and all the young turtles work together to open the nest.

Eggs and hatchlings are heavily preyed upon by raccoons, dogs, vultures, and other scavengers.

Only two nests are known from Florida.

Lepidochelys kempii (Garman) **Atlantic Ridley**

Description: The ridley is a comparatively small sea turtle, reaching a maximum length of 27 inches (70 cm), with a heart-shaped, olive-green carapace which, in adults, is often wider than it is long. The double-keeled plastron is yellow or bleached white. The head and flippers are olive in adults, and gray in

108   The Turtles—Cheloniids

PETER C. H. PRITCHARD

Atlantic ridley

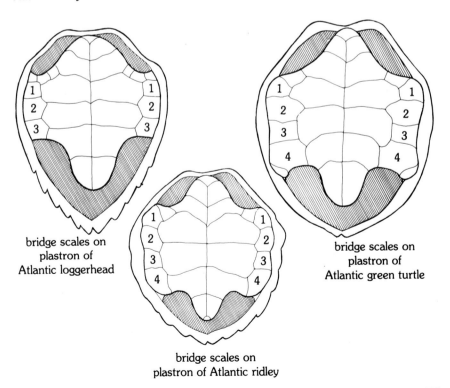

bridge scales on
plastron of
Atlantic loggerhead

bridge scales on
plastron of
Atlantic green turtle

bridge scales on
plastron of Atlantic ridley

The Turtles—Cheloniids

juveniles. The four scales on the bridge between the plastron and carapace have obvious holes or pores. There is a tiny scale on the posterior end of the plastron.

Juveniles: Juveniles are dark gray to black with white-edged flippers and carapace. The plastron is dark in hatchlings, getting lighter with age, and has four longitudinal ridges or keels.

Similar Species: The larger loggerhead is reddish brown and has three or four scales on the bridge which lack pores.

Range of the Atlantic Ridley in Florida is in the Gulf of Mexico and along the Atlantic coast.

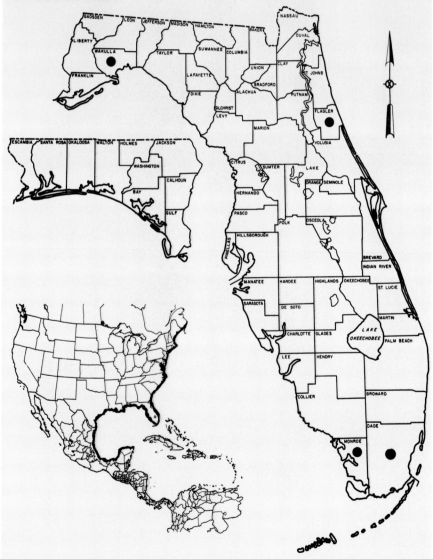

The Turtles—Cheloniids

Natural History: For a long time, this turtle was thought to be a cross between the loggerhead and green turtle and was known as the bastard turtle, but it is a species in its own right. The ridley is primarily carnivorous, feeding on crabs, mollusks, and fish.

Little is known about the movements of this species, as is the case in all sea turtles, but it is believed that they travel mostly in the coastal waters of the Gulf of Mexico. Occasionally, young ridleys are observed in the Crystal River and Cedar Key area. Rarely, adults have been observed along the Atlantic coast.

Heavy collecting of adults and eggs has caused this species to become the most endangered of the sea turtles.

Reproduction: The ridley is not known to breed in Florida, but does breed in southern Texas and Tamaulipas, Mexico. Breeding and nesting occur in April through August on sandy beaches during the day. Up to three trips may be made by a single female to the nesting site. When digging the nest, first the front flippers are used to dig a body pit. The turtle, with its whole body in this shallow pit, then uses its hind flippers to scoop out the egg cavity. Often more than 100 eggs are laid; they take up to 60 days to hatch.

Chelydra serpentina (Linnaeus) **Common Snapping Turtle**

Description: This large common aquatic turtle may reach a length of 18.5 inches (47 cm) and weigh 45 pounds (34 kg) or more. The carapace, head, legs, and tail are a uniform gray-brown to brown color. The small plastron and adjoining skin are light yellow to cream. The carapace may have low bumps or may be smooth with a jagged hind edge. The tail is long and has three rows of large hard knobs extending down its length. The head is large and the neck is long.

WILLIAM B. and KATHLEEN V. LOVE

common snapping turtle

The Turtles—Chelydrids

Juveniles: The carapace is very rough and has two deep grooves on each side of the center. The carapace is dark gray and the plastron is black with white spots. The tail is long and lacks the large bumps of the adult. They may easily be mistaken for juvenile alligator snappers.

Similar Species: The alligator snapper has large ridges on the carapace,

Range of the Florida Snapping Turtle in Florida is designated by the open area, Common Snapping Turtle by the ▓▓ area. Insert map shows general distribution of the species in the United States.

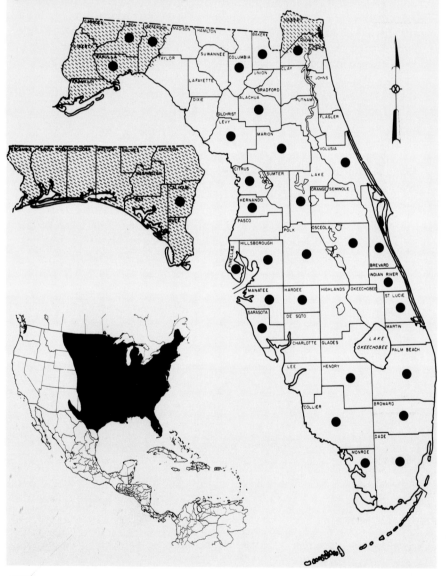

The Turtles—Chelydrids

and a shorter tail without bony bumps. The upper jaw of the alligator snapper has a hawk-like beak.

Natural History: The snapping turtle gets its name from its lightning-like bite and its strong jaws, which are capable of doing serious damage. When alarmed, snapping turtles release a strong anal musk. This species is commonly found in nearly all bodies of fresh water and is often taken for its tasty meat.

Although seen traveling across the ground during rains, the snapping turtle is one of the most aquatic turtles, rarely climbing out to bask like other water turtles, but, instead, basking by floating on the surface of the water. It searches the bottom for food, which includes aquatic invertebrates, dead animals, fish, frogs, aquatic birds, snakes or any other animal that gets within range of those powerful jaws. Adults may sit under banks or root stumps in ambush. The snapper is also known for taking waterfowl and wading birds.

Snappers are active mostly at night; during the day they hide among tree roots or undercut banks. They rarely move out of a definite home range within a pool or section of marsh.

Reproduction: Mating occurs from April to November. Nesting occurs from May to September. Females may move a good distance from the water to dig their nest. Nests and, possibly in some cases, a body cavity are dug with the hind feet in loamy soils. Nests may be up to 7 inches (18 cm) deep and contain 11-83 white spherical eggs. Nearly half of all nests are destroyed by egg-eating mammals like raccoons and skunks. Eggs hatch in 55-125 days, either hatching in late summer or overwintering to the following spring.

Subspecies: *Chelydra serpentina osceola* (Stejneger) **Florida Snapping Turtle** This snapper is hard to distinguish from the common snapper; however, it is considered to be a full species by some herpetologists. It differs in having long spine-like tubercles at the base of the head and neck and also differs in some scalation. This form may have a light-colored upper jaw.

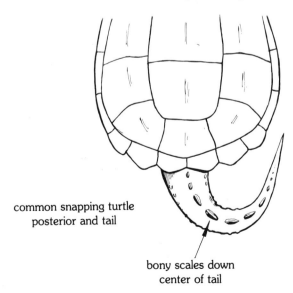

common snapping turtle
posterior and tail

bony scales down
center of tail

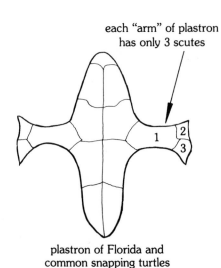

each "arm" of plastron
has only 3 scutes

1 2 3

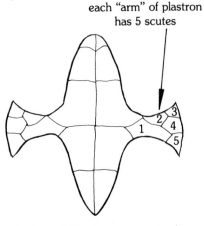

each "arm" of plastron
has 5 scutes

1 2 3 4 5

plastron of Florida and
common snapping turtles

plastron of alligator snapping turtle

Macroclemys temmincki (Troost)
Alligator Snapping Turtle

Description: One of the largest freshwater turtles in the world, the alligator snapper may reach a length of 28 inches (71 cm) and a weight of over 200 pounds (91 kg). The dark brown carapace has three rows of large knobs or ridges and a jagged rear edge. The tail is long and rounded. The head is very large, and the neck is short. The upper jaw has a hawk-like beak. The dark plastron is greatly reduced. The tongue ends in a red worm-like "fishing lure".

Juveniles: They are similar to adults, except they are brown to gray in color and the carapace is rougher. The neck and head are covered with fleshy

JOSEPH T. COLLINS

alligator snapping turtle

The Turtles—Chelydrids

tubercles. Juveniles have been reported to use their long tails to hold onto objects.

Similar Species: The common snapping turtle lacks ridges on the carapace and the pointed, hooked beak. The common snapper has bony ridges along the tail which the alligator snapper lacks.

Range of the Alligator Snapping Turtle in Florida. Insert map shows general distribution of the species in the United States.

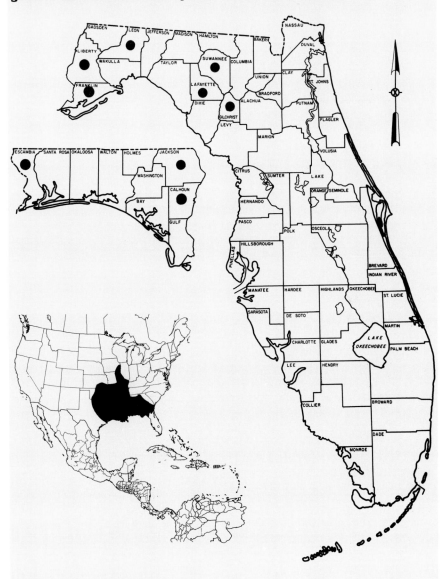

alligator snapping turtle—note tongue "lure"

Natural History: The alligator snapper occurs from the Santa Fe and Suwannee Rivers west through the panhandle. It inhabits sloughs, lakes and slow moving waters, but does not live in swifter waters. Very little is known about this huge turtle. Rarely coming out of the water, the alligator snapper may creep along the bottom of freshwater rivers, swamps, and lakes at night in search of food. Or, the camouflaged snapper will sit on the bottom and lure fish into its gaping jaws by flicking the bright red worm-like tongue. Food includes anything that can be subdued by the powerful jaws; they are also scavengers and feed on carrion.

Care should be taken when handling a captured specimen since the jaws can inflict serious wounds. This species is protected from commercial collecting or exportation in Florida.

Reproduction: Mating occurs in February, March, and April. Nesting begins in April and last through the spring. The female digs a flask-shaped pit with her hind legs. The nest is dug on dry land above the water line. The eggs are spherical and have a hard, smooth, white shell. Clutches may contain 16-50 eggs which will hatch in 100-142 days.

Dermochelys coriacea coriacea   (Linnaeus)
Atlantic Leatherback

Description: This is the largest living species of turtle, weighing up to 1,600 pounds (726 kg) and reaching up to 96 inches (244 cm) in length. It is easily recognized because the shell is covered with a leathery hide. The oblong carapace has five longitudinal ridges. The head and neck are black to gray or dark brown. There is a tooth-like projection on each side of the upper jaw. The flippers lack claws.

Juveniles: Hatchlings are black with the carapace ridges spotted with white. The back edges of the front flippers and the edges surrounding the back flippers are white.

Similar Species: All other sea turtles have a hard, bony shell covered with plates.

Range of the Atlantic Leatherback in Florida is in the warm waters of the Atlantic and Gulf of Mexico.

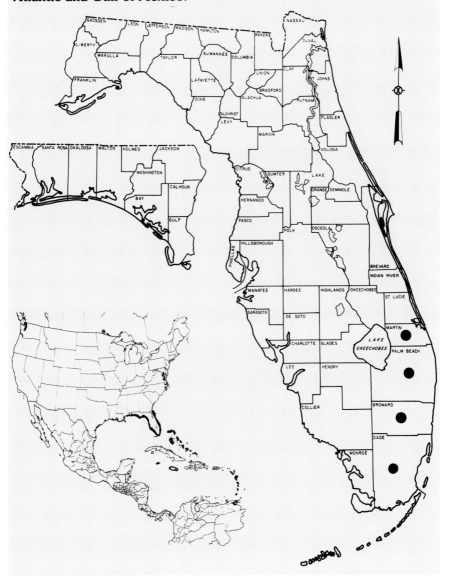

PETER C. H. PRITCHARD

Atlantic leatherback

Natural History: Little is known about this species' habits since it is rarely encountered. Adults are probably omnivorous, feeding on jellyfish, sea urchins, squid, algae, and seaweed. They are seen sometimes in groups, far out at sea. This species has a reputation for being vicious when captured. It is considered endangered and is protected.

Reproduction: Nesting rarely occurs in Florida today. However, there are reports that at one time the leatherback nested here in large numbers, especially in the keys. Leatherbacks nest in the spring and summer months. With their powerful front flippers, they dig out an area large enough to accommodate the whole body. Inside this pit, the egg cavity is dug by the hind flippers. The pit and egg cavity may be 3 feet (1 m) in total depth. The female lays 86 or more ovoid white eggs in the nest, which is then covered. Hatching occurs in 60-68 days.

Chrysemys concinna suwanniensis   (Carr)
Suwannee Cooter

Description: The carapace may reach a length of 16 inches (41 cm) and is dark with a faint reticulated pattern. The second costal scute has a "C" in the upper corner. The nearly black head has faint yellow stripes. The front feet have two or three yellow stripes, but the hind feet lack the yellow markings on the top. The plastron is yellow to orange with a well developed pattern of gray or black markings.

Juveniles: The juveniles have head and feet patterns similar to adults. The carapace is yellow around the edge and heavily patterned with green-brown blotches bordered with bright yellow. The plastron is light orange or yellow in color with a central dark blotch.

The Turtles—Emydids

Suwannee cooter

Similar Species: The Florida cooter has open circles where the carapace meets the bridge; the redbelly turtle has wide reddish lines on the carapace scutes; and the peninsula cooter has a plain plastron.

Natural History: This species is found in the lower drainages and river mouths from Hillsborough County to Gulf County. It is frequently seen basking in large numbers on overhanging logs. Unlike most water turtles, this cooter will not travel away from the water except to nest. It seems to be highly tolerant of changes in salinity and can be found in bays and lagoons.

Adults feed mainly on turtle grass or other aquatic vegetation and may

Chrysemys sp. laying eggs

The Turtles—Emydids   119

occasionally feed on carrion. Juveniles feed on insects and other forms of small aquatic life.

Adults are collected for food and are often shot by vandals while basking. This species is considered threatened in Florida.

Reproduction: Until recently, the nesting habits of the Suwannee cooter were unknown. It was discovered that the female nests during late summer in

Range of the Mobile Cooter in Florida is designated by the open area, Suwanne Cooter by the ⁞⁞⁞ area. Insert map shows general distribution of the species in the United States.

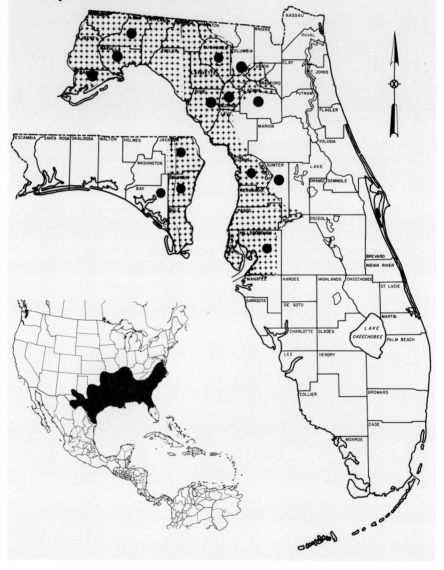

The Turtles—Emydids

Mobile cooter

sandy soil near a river bank. She digs a central nest with a false nest on each side. These false nests are rarely covered and one or two eggs are deposited in them to distract predators away from the main nest. The center nest contains the main clutch of eggs numbering 20 or more. This nest is usually thoroughly covered. Hatching takes place in 84-92 days.

Subspecies: *Chrysemys concinna mobilensis* (Holbrook) **Mobile Cooter** The carapace is high, broad, and light to dark brown in color. The stripes on the head are yellow to reddish. The outer surfaces of the limbs are lined with yellow. This subspecies is found west of the Apalachicola River.

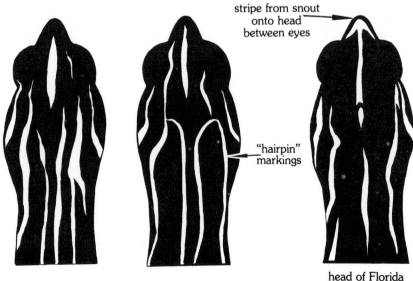

stripe from snout onto head between eyes

"hairpin" markings

head of Suwannee cooter

head of peninsula cooter

head of Florida redbelly turtle

The Turtles—Emydids

Chrysemys floridana peninsularis Carr **Peninsula Cooter**

Description: This common aquatic turtle may reach a maximum length of 15 inches (38 cm). The carapace is dark and heavily marked with narrow yellowish stripes on each scute. The plastron is yellow and unmarked. The head is black with yellow stripes. The markings on the top of the head are hairpin shaped. The legs are heavily striped with yellow.

Juveniles: The head markings are like the adults'. The carapace has a yellow border and is marked with green and brown. The plastron is yellow with dark round dots on the edge near the bridge.

Similar Species: The Suwannee cooter lacks "hairpins" and has a "C" marking on the second costal scale.

Natural History: Peninsula cooters are commonly seen basking on logs and banks and are active primarily during the day, resting at the water's bottom

ZIG LESZCZYNSKI

peninsula cooter

ZIG LESZCZYNSKI

juvenile peninsula cooter

The Turtles—Emydids

during the night. They inhabit lakes and slow-moving streams with abundant vegetation and soft sandy bottoms, particularly along the St. John's drainage. Peninsula cooters migrate from one body of water to another and are often seen crossing highways. Adult cooters feed primarily on aquatic vegetation. Juveniles feed on aquatic insects. Cooters are commonly taken for food.

Range of the Peninsula Cooter in Florida is designated by the open area, Florida Cooter by the ▨ area. Insert map shows general distribution of the species in the United States.

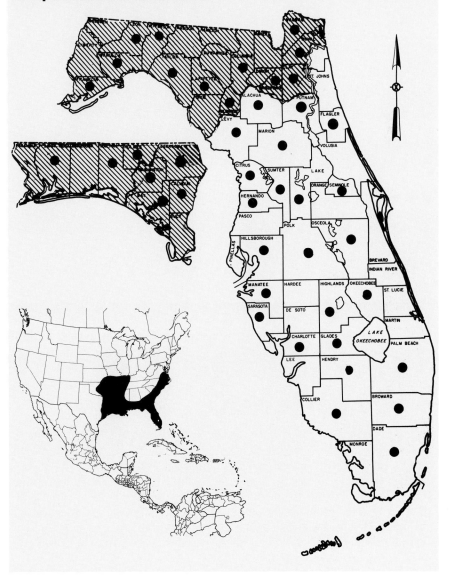

Florida cooter

Reproduction: Nesting occurs throughout the year. Nests are built in open places in sandy loam soil, not far from the shoreline. The female digs the nest with her hind legs. It is flask shaped and has a false nest on each side, several inches away. The false nests may be empty or may contain two or three eggs. The central main nest may contain 12-29 elliptical, white, hard-shelled eggs. Eggs hatch in 80-150 days, occasionally they may overwinter.

Subspecies: *Chrysemys floridana floridana* (Le Conte) **Florida Cooter** This subspecies does not have the "hairpins" on the head but does have the stripes. The raised carapace is usually dark with faint yellowish markings. The underside of the carapace is marked with green circles. The plastron is bright yellow in color and lacks markings. The head and feet are dark brown marked with bright yellow.

Chrysemys nelsoni (Carr) **Florida Redbelly Turtle**

Description: This large turtle grows to 13 inches (34 cm) in shell length. The carapace is dark, nearly black, with a rusty-red wash appearance and often with faded, wide reddish markings. Margins of the shell are reddish or coppery in color. The plastron is rusty red or orange. The head is black with bright yellow stripes which extend onto the snout. The black feet and tail are striped with yellow. One short yellow stripe runs from the snout over the head and between the eyes. The upper jaw is notched and has a cusp on either side.

Juveniles: The carapace is slightly keeled in the young. The plastron is orange and may be marked with dark half-moon spots.

The Turtles—Emydids

Similar Species: Cooters lack the cusps on the sides of the notched upper jaw, and the short stripe between the eyes.

Natural History: This species prefers fresh to brackish water with little or no flow and abundant vegetation, and is found in spring runs within its range. The redbelly turtle spends a great deal of time basking along with the yellowbelly slider. Adults feed primarily on aquatic plants, including the leaves of water

Range of the Florida Redbelly Turtle in Florida. Insert map shows general distribution of the species in the United States.

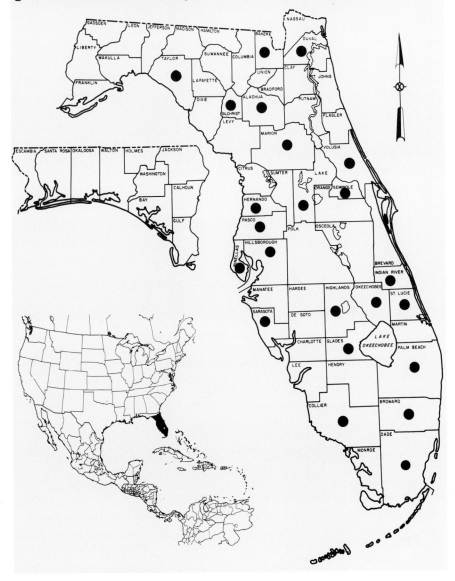

Florida redbelly turtle

hyacinths, but will also take carrion. Juveniles probably feed on aquatic insects, other small animals, and plants.

Adult redbelly turtles are fed upon by man and alligators, and the juveniles are eaten by wading birds, skunks, raccoons, opossums, fish and other turtles.

Reproduction: Nesting occurs in late spring to early summer, possibly throughout the year. Twelve to 30 or more elliptical eggs are laid in the underground nest cavity which is dug by the female, often some distance from the water. The redbelly turtle often lays its eggs in alligator nests.

Note: Chrysemys alabamensis (Baur) **Alabama Redbelly Turtle** Questionable records of this species have been reported from Wakulla and Franklin counties. There is some doubt that this species occurs in Florida; the specimens are probably the very similar Florida redbelly turtle (*C. nelsoni*). The Alabama redbelly turtle has a complex pattern of head stripes and a reddish plastron. This species inhabits coastal saltwater and freshwater marshes along the Tensaw River.

Chrysemys scripta scripta (Schoeff) **Yellowbelly Slider**

Description: This medium sized slider reaches a maximum length of 11 inches (29 cm), but is usually less than 9 inches (23 cm). The dark carapace has broad yellowish-brown vertical bars on the large scales. The plastron is yellow with brown smudges. The black head has a broad yellow blotch behind each eye. The front legs are marked with narrow yellow stripes; the hind legs are marked with "striped pants".

The Turtles—Emydids

yellowbelly slider

juvenile yellowbelly slider

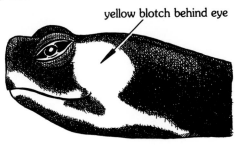

yellow blotch behind eye

yellowbelly slider

Juveniles: The carapace is green with faint yellowish stripes and edged in yellow. The plastron is yellow with round spots on the anterior scutes. The head is marked with orange-yellow patches behind each eye.

Similar Species: The chicken turtle has "striped pants" on the hind legs, but has a single broad stripe on each front leg, and its head has narrow stripes and lacks the large blotches behind the eye.

Range of the Yellowbelly Slider in Florida. Insert map shows general distribution of the species in the United States.

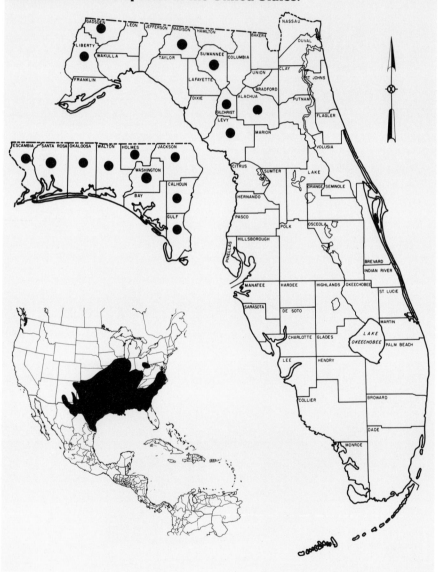

The Turtles—Emydids

Natural History: The yellowbelly slider is found primarily in ponds, lakes, or streams that have a lot of aquatic vegetation, or in sterile sinkholes and ponds. It is most commonly observed while basking on logs or vegetation mats, usually singly or in small numbers. This species of turtle commonly migrates across land, especially during the spring and late summer.

Young sliders feed mainly on aquatic insects and other invertebrates. As they grow older, their diet changes to include more vegetation; small vertebrates and invertebrates are also taken.

Small turtles do well in captivity if fed a mixed diet of lettuce and chicken parts or canned dog food. A dry basking site and occasional sun should be provided.

Predators, including alligators, raccoons, and herons, especially favor the young turtles and turtle eggs. Adults are preyed upon by man.

Reproduction: Females may wander some distance from the water in search of proper soil conditions in which to dig the flask-shaped nests. After the nest is dug with the hind feet, 4-9 white oval eggs are laid. The nest is then covered. Nesting takes place from early spring into summer or early fall with each female probably nesting twice a year. Hatching occurs in 2-3 months.

Clemmys guttata   (Schneider)   **Spotted Turtle**

Description: This small turtle may reach 5 inches (13 cm) in shell length. The smooth carapace, legs, and head are black and spotted with yellow. The scales on the unhinged black plastron are edged with yellow or cream.

Juveniles: Juveniles are black and may lack or have reduced spotting on the shell.

spotted turtle

Similar Species: None.

Natural History: Although several individuals have been collected in Florida, the spotted turtle's presence here as a native species is questionable. The turtles may have been escaped captives. However, the slow-moving woodland or meadow streams with sphagnum that it inhabits in the north do occur in north Florida, making its presence possible.

Range of the Spotted Turtle in Florida. Insert map shows general distribution of the species in the United States.

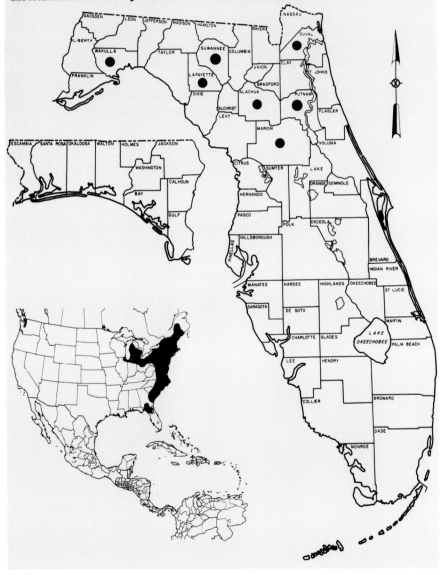

The Turtles—Emydids

Spotted turtles feed on insects, other aquatic invertebrates, and occasionally vegetation. They are at home on land as well as in streams. They commonly bask on logs or on the stream edge.

Reproduction: Courtship and mating occur in early spring in the northern part of its range. The flask-shaped nests are made on dry open land, and are covered well after the eggs are deposited. After checking the soil with her front feet, the female may dig a few trial nests before the actual nest is finally dug with the hind feet. The 3-5 white eggs are elliptical and have rubbery shells. Incubation requires 70-80 days; hatching occurs in August.

Deirochelys reticularia chrysea (Schwartz)
Florida Chicken Turtle

Description: This oblong turtle may reach a length of 10 inches (25 cm). The green carapace is marked with a yellowish net-like pattern except in older adults. The edge of the shell is bordered in orange or yellow. The plastron and underside of the carapace are yellow and lack any markings. The neck is very long and striped with yellow. The front legs are marked with one wide stripe, but there are "striped pants" on the hind legs. Either side of the tail is marked with vertical yellow stripes.

Juveniles: Juveniles are marked like the adults, except the markings are brighter and the shell is edged with bright yellow.

Similar Species: The yellowbelly slider has a wide shell and yellow blotches on the head.

WILLIAM B. and KATHLEEN V. LOVE

Florida chicken turtle

Natural History: This turtle is commonly observed while basking or crossing the highways, especially during the spring. Little is known about the habits of this turtle. They apparently feed on small forms of aquatic life including crayfish, tadpoles and carrion. They inhabit the quiet waters of ponds, marshes and sloughs.

Range of the Florida Chicken Turtle in Florida is designated by the open area, Eastern Chicken Turtle by the ⁙ area. Insert map shows general distribution of the species in the United States.

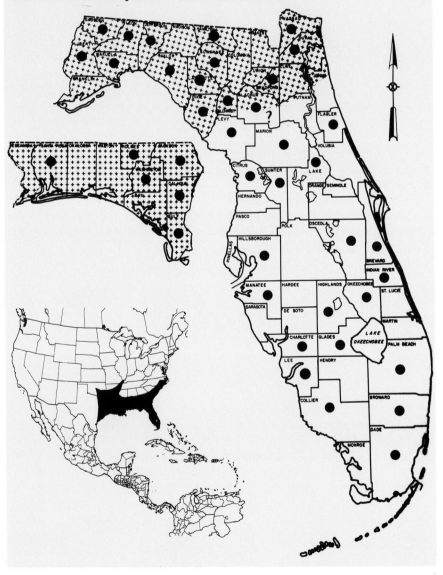

The Turtles—Emydids

eastern chicken turtle

Reproduction: Nesting may occur throughout the year. Nests are dug in soil with the hind legs, not too far from the shoreline, and are approximately 4 inches (10 cm) deep and 3 inches (8 cm) in diameter at the top. Seven to 15 elliptical white eggs are deposited in the nest. Eggs hatch in approximately three months.

Supspecies: Deirochelys reticularia reticularia (Latreille) **Eastern Chicken Turtle** The upper shell is dark green or brown with a very faint reticulated pattern and has a yellowish rim around the edge. The plastron is yellow. The underside of the carapace edge is spotted. The neck is long with narrow yellow stripes. This subspecies occurs in the northern part of the state.

Graptemys barbouri Carr and Marchand
Barbour's Map Turtle

Description: There is a considerable size difference between the sexes: males reach a maximum length of 5 inches (13 cm), and the females reach a length of 12 inches (30 cm). The carapace has a dorsal keel with black-tipped knobs. The rear edge of the carapace is jagged or saw-toothed. The carapace is olive gray to dark brown in color with dull yellow "U" shaped marks on each scute. The plastron is greenish yellow to cream colored with scales bordered with black. The head is marked with three large light patches, one on the snout and one behind each eye. There are several pin stripes on the head and a light bar along the curve of the jaw. Females have extremely large heads, while males have much smaller, narrow, rounded heads.

Juveniles: The carapace is saw-backed with orange "C" shaped markings on some scales. The plastron is yellowish to white. There are broad light areas on the chin and behind each eye.

The Turtles—Emydids

Similar Species: Cooters lack the dorsal keel.

Natural History: The Barbour's map turtle is found in the Chipola and Apalachicola Rivers in Florida. Map turtles live in a home range of a few hundred square yards. This shy turtle is most often observed from a distance while it basks on logs or floats on the surface. At the slightest disturbance, it submerges. Females have flat crushing jaws, which are used in feeding on snails

Range of Barbour's Map Turtle in Florida. Insert map shows general distribution of the species in the United States.

The Turtles—Emydids

Barbour's map turtle

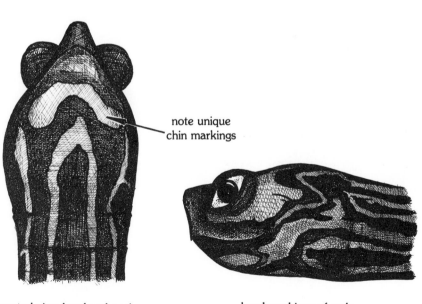

note unique
chin markings

ventral view head and neck
Barbour's map turtle

head markings of male
Barbour's map turtle

The Turtles—Emydids

and clams. Males lack the crushing jaws and feed on live caddis fly larvae and other invertebrates.

Barbour's map turtles are collected for food, and are also shot by vandals while sunning. This species of turtle may be threatened by such pressure along with stream modifications like channelization or damming in its limited range.

Reproduction: Females may deposit as many as 50 or more eggs per year, possibly in three or more nests. Nesting occurs from May through June. Four to 11 eggs are laid in each nest, which is made close to the water's edge.

During courtship, the male approaches the female with his neck extended until they are face to face. After nose contact, he strokes her head with the inner side of his forelegs. If the female is responsive to the male's overture, then breeding takes place. Sexual maturity is reached in 20 years by females, and in three years by males.

Graptemys pulchra (Baur) **Alabama Map Turtle**

Description: The smaller males may reach a length of 5.5 inches (14 cm), while the females may reach 11.5 inches (29 cm) in length. The carapace of the males and some females is strongly keeled. The keel may have several raised, dark knobs. The carapace is brown to olive with a median black stripe. The head is marked with large yellow or greenish blotches behind the eyes and on top of the head and snout. The neck is marked with broad yellow or orange stripes. The larger females have enlarged heads and crushing plates. The plastron is yellow white, without markings.

Juveniles: The plastron is yellow, sometimes with blotches. The carapace is greenish to olive with reddish "C" shaped markings on some scutes.

WILLIAM B. and KATHLEEN V. LOVE

Alabama map turtle

The Turtles—Emydids

Similar Species: Barbour's map turtles are similar, however, the ranges are very restricted in both species.

Natural History: This turtle spends much of its time basking on logs, and its home range may be only a few hundred square yards. The food of the females consists of snails, clams, mollusks and insects. The males feed on insects, fish and probably carrion. This species is quite common within its range, which only

Range of the Alabama Map Turtle in Florida. Insert map shows general distribution of the species in the United States.

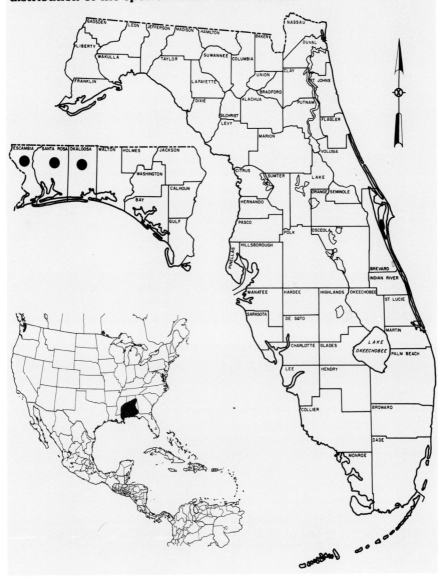

note long light bar
on chin which may extend
longitudinally along the neck

ventral view head and neck
Alabama map turtle

head striping of the
Alabama map turtle

includes the far western panhandle in Florida. It requires about 14 years for a female to become sexually mature, but only five years for the male.

Reproduction: Females probably lay 6-7 clutches a year, with 6-13 eggs in each flask-shaped nest. Exposed sandbars are favored nesting sites. Nesting begins in April and continues through July.

Malaclemys terrapin (Schoepff) **Diamondback Terrapin**

Description: This medium sized turtle reaches a length of 9 inches (23 cm) and has a gray to black carapace. The skin on the head and feet is smoky gray with variable spotting. (See subspecies identifications.) The plastron is creamy yellow and covers most of the underside of the turtle.

Juveniles: Similar to adults but with circular rings on each of the scales of the carapace.

Similar Species: None.

Natural History: This highly edible species historically was found in most coastal marshes, estuaries, and lagoons all around the Florida coasts, including the keys. However, these once common turtles have been greatly reduced in number in many areas primarily because of coastal building developments and other habitat destruction. Market hunting of adults and eggs may also be another reason for the decline.

During the day the terrapin basks or searches for food, which includes carrion, snails, crabs, and other invertebrates, as well as marsh plants. They may venture into grassy lowlands during high tides in search of insects.

Terrapins are adapted for living in salt water. They can secrete excess salt through glands near the eye.

138 The Turtles—Emydids

Reproduction: Mating occurs in the water, soon after the turtles emerge from their winter retreats. Nesting occurs from early spring into summer. Nests are made in dry sand above the high tide line on sand dunes and offshore islands. The triangular nest is dug by the female with the hind feet. The bladder is usually voided during the digging to moisten the loose sand in the nest area. Four to 12 eggs are laid in the nest. One female may nest several times in one year, and is capable of laying up to 35 eggs per year even at 25 years of age. The eggs are oblong, pinkish white and thin shelled. Eggs hatch in about 3 months.

R. W. VAN DEVENDER

Carolina diamondback terrapin

ZIG LESZCZYNSKI

Florida east coast
diamondback terrapin

Range of the Mississippi Diamondback Terrapin (A) in Florida. Range of the Ornate Diamondback Terrapin (B) in Florida. Range of the Mangrove Diamondback Terrapin (C) in Florida. Range of the Florida East Coast Diamondback Terrapin (D) in Florida. Range of the Carolina Diamondback Terrapin (E) in Florida. Insert map shows general distribution of the species in the United States.

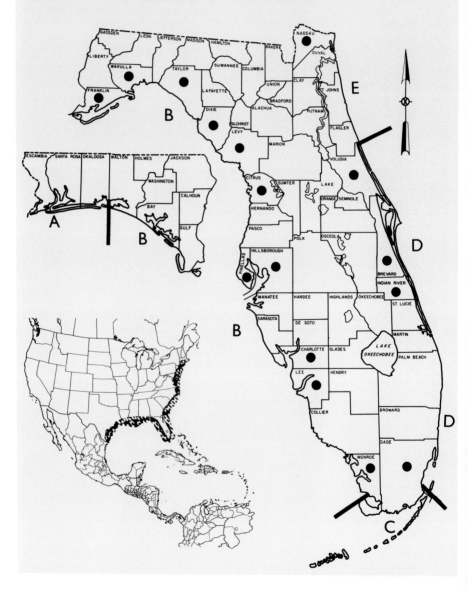

The Turtles—Emydids

mangrove diamondback terrapin

ornate diamondback terrapin

Subspecies:

Malaclemys terrapin centrata (Latreille) **Carolina Diamondback Terrapin** The carapace is broad, and black or brown in color with faint or no markings. The head is broad and flat, especially in the female. The lips and top of the head are white or dusky gray. The skin is gray green between each scale. The plastron is yellowish or green with concentric rings.

Malaclemys terrapin tequesta Schwartz **Florida East Coast Diamond-**

The Turtles—Emydids   141

Mississippi diamondback terrapin

back Terrapin The oblong carapace is dark and lacks markings or growth rings. The center of each scale may have a light area or spot.

Malaclemys terrapin rhizophorarum Fowler **Mangrove Diamondback Terrapin** The carapace has a low, expanded keel with raised bumps. Light spots on the scales of the carapace are absent but there are concentric light and dark rings. The spots on the head are fused into blotches.

Malaclemys terrapin macrospilota Hay **Ornate Diamondback Terrapin** The scales of the carapace are heavily ridged and each has a yellow-orange spot in the center. The head is gray with a few large spots.

Malaclemys terrapin pileata (Wied) **Mississippi Diamondback Terrapin** The carapace is oval and is black or brown with black dorsal bumps along the central keel. The head is spotted and the lips are dusky in color.

Terrapene carolina bauri Taylor **Florida Box Turtle**

Description: The carapace is domed, narrow, and up to 6.5 inches (16.5 cm) in length. Each carapace scute is usually black with bright radiating yellow stripes. The plastron has one hinge which permits the shell to close tightly. Males have a depression in the posterior section of the plastron. The head is dark with two yellow stripes extending along each side. The hind feet usually have three long-clawed toes. Markings are extremely variable.

Juveniles: The carapace is dark with a bright dorsal stripe along the central ridge.

142

The Turtles—Emydids

Florida box turtle

Similar Species: The gulf coast box turtle lacks the strong yellowish markings and the stripes on the head.

Natural History: Commonly found in mesic hammocks and pine flatwoods, the Florida box turtle is most commonly observed crossing highways. The box turtle feeds on plants, including fungi (some toxic forms, which do not harm the turtle), insects, carrion, dung, and some small vertebrates. They may be commonly seen in streams or ponds, possibly soaking or drinking. Box turtles make shallow holes about the size of their shell during periods of inactivity. They back into these pits which are in the soil just below leaf litter. In captivity, they were observed to return to the same pits at night. Studies of the related ornate box turtle have shown that they have small

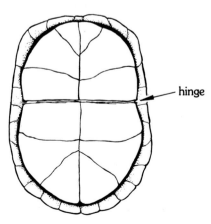

box turtle plastron with hinge

The Turtles—Emydids   143

juvenile Florida box turtle

home ranges that contain several of these pits which are commonly utilized. Also, the populations are rather stable with few juveniles present at any one time.

Box turtles do well in captivity but should have water to soak in and a varied diet. There is some indication that box turtles are toxic and should not be eaten. This toxicity is due to the stored toxins which accumulate from eating toxic fungi.

Reproduction: Breeding and nesting occur in late spring and early summer. A pit-like nest is dug with the hind legs, and 3-7 oblong, soft-shelled white eggs are laid before the nest is well covered by the female. The eggs hatch in about two months.

Terrapene carolina major (Agassiz) **Gulf Coast Box Turtle**

Description: The largest box turtle in Florida, it may attain a shell length of 8.5 inches (22 cm). Usually the carapace is dark chocolate brown to black, with other markings absent or very faint. The carapace is high domed and flared at the back. The hinged plastron is usually brown anteriorly and yellow or tan posteriorly and can close tightly against the carapace. The head is marked with irregular yellow stripes; in some locations old males may have cream colored heads. There are usually three toes on each hind foot.

Juveniles: The carapace and head are black or brown. The shell is flattened and marked with yellow spots on the sides and down the center of the back. The plastron is marked with a yellow ring around a dark brown center.

144   The Turtles—Emydids

Range of the Florida Box Turtle in Florida is designated by the open area, Gulf Coast Box Turtle by the ⧄ area, Eastern Box Turtle by the ⠿ area, Three-toed Box Turtle by the ⬡ area. Insert map shows general distribution of the species in the United States.

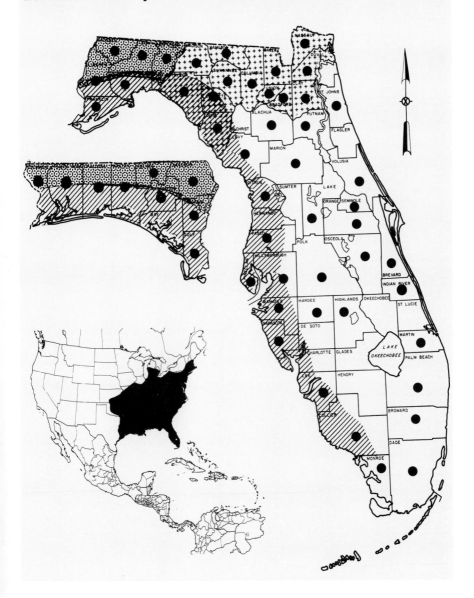

Similar Species: The Florida box turtle is black with bold radiating yellow markings on each scute of the carapace, and usually has four toes on each hind foot.

Natural History: Found most commonly in upland hammocks and flat-woods, the gulf coast box turtle is locally common. Like most box turtles, they are found around streams or wet areas. During periods of inactivity, such as very hot and dry periods, this turtle will burrow shallowly below the leaf litter. During the day the box turtle forages for a variety of foods, including insects and

gulf coast box turtle

old male gulf coast box turtle

The Turtles—Emydids

three-toed box turtle

other invertebrates, plants (berries, mosses, grasses), carrion, and dung. Adults live in a relatively small home range. Box turtles are often kept as pets. They should be given a pan of water for soaking and a variety of foods including canned dog food or cat food.

Reproduction: Mating and nesting probably occur from June through the summer. Nests are usually made in open upland areas. The flask-shaped nests are made with the hind feet. After 3-7 eggs are laid, the female fills the nest using her hind feet and tamps down the fill with the plastron and all four feet. The elliptical eggs have flexible white shells and hatch in about three months.

Subspecies:

Terrapene carolina carolina (Linnaeus) **Eastern Box Turtle** The box turtles of the northeastern counties show characteristics of this race. There are usually four toes on each hind foot. The color of the shell is highly variable with yellow or orange blotches on each scute. The plastron is yellow to brown.

Terrapene carolina triunguis (Agassiz) **Three-toed Box Turtle** The three-toed box turtle has three toes on each hind foot. The carapace is usually brown or olive with very faint or no stripes or blotches. The influence of this race is seen in the box turtles in the northern counties of the panhandle.

Kinosternon bauri palmarum Stejneger **Striped Mud Turtle**

Description: This small turtle, nearly 5 inches (12 cm) in length, has an oval, dome-shaped carapace usually with three yellowish to brownish stripes on a black to dark brown background. The plastron is olive to yellow with each scale surrounded in dark brown. The small rounded head has two faint stripes behind and below each eye. The lower jaw is faintly striped or mottled.

Juveniles: Juveniles are black with yellow spots along the edge of the shell. The carapace has three yellow longitudinal stripes. The plastron is yellow,

The Turtles—Kinosternids

147

bordered with dark brown and with a brown spot in the center. The stripes on the head are quite distinct.

Similar Species: The musk turtle lacks stripes on the carapace and has skin between the scales of the plastron.

Range of the Striped Mud Turtle in Florida is designated by the open area. Key Mud Turtle is restricted to the lower keys below the line. Insert map shows general distribution of the species in the United States.

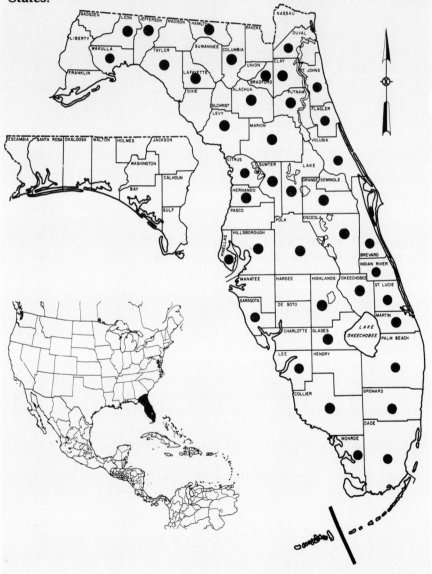

The Turtles—Kinosternids

striped mud turtle (underwater)

Natural History: Found in shallow marshes, cypress heads, and other shallow water habitats, the striped mud turtle frequently wanders on dry land.

This species seems to be mild mannered compared to other mud and musk turtles. They feed on plant material as well as small aquatic animals and carrion, and are easily trapped or captured with a meat-baited hook. This species does well in captivity.

Reproduction: Courtship and nesting generally occur from March to October, but may occur throughout the year. Nests are built in sandpiles or decaying vegetation near the shoreline. One to five (usually 2-3) elliptical, brittle, whitish eggs are laid in each nest, with three or more nests being made by the female over the year. Hatching occurs in 3-4 months.

Subspecies: *Kinosternon bauri bauri* (Garman) **Key Mud Turtle** Found in the lower keys from Big Pine Key to Key West, the key mud turtle is the only small aquatic turtle in the area. Found in freshwater pools and ponds, it may wander onto land and into brackish water. This questionable subspecies is considered threatened due to habitat destruction. The scales of the carapace are dark with stripes nearly or completely lacking. The lower jaw lacks the stripes found in the striped mud turtle.

Kinosternon subrubrum steindachneri (Siebenrock) **Florida Mud Turtle**

Description: This mud turtle is 5 inches (13 cm) long, with a small, smooth, oblong-shaped shell. The carapace is blackish or dark brown and unmarked. The posterior lobes of the plastron are much narrower in this subspecies. The yellowish-tan plastron covers most of the underside and has two hinges which allow the shell to partially close. The large head is either mottled or slightly spotted. The jaws are lighter than the dark head.

The Turtles—Kinosternids

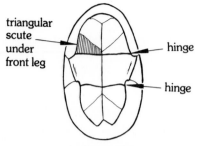

triangular
scute
under
front leg

hinge

hinge

striped mud turtle plastron
note two hinges

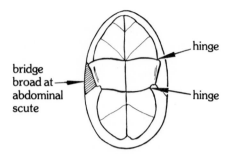

hinge

bridge
broad at
abdominal
scute

hinge

Florida mud turtle plastron
note two hinges

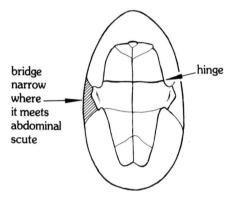

bridge
narrow
where
it meets
abdominal
scute

hinge

loggerhead musk turtle plastron
note one hinge and broad bridge

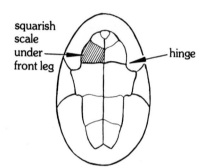

squarish
scale
under
front leg

hinge

stinkpot plastron
one hinge and there may be
skin between plastron scutes

ROBERT S. SIMMONS

Florida mud turtle

The Turtles—Kinosternids

Juveniles: The edge of the shell is yellowish or pink. The plastron is pink or red with a brown or black blotch in the center.

Similar Species: The striped mud turtle has longitudinal stripes on the shell. Stinkpots have distinct stripes on the head, and the loggerhead musk turtles have exposed skin between the scales of the plastron.

Range of the Florida Mud Turtle in Florida is designated by the open area, Eastern Mud Turtle by the ▒▒ area. Insert map shows general distribution of the species in the United States.

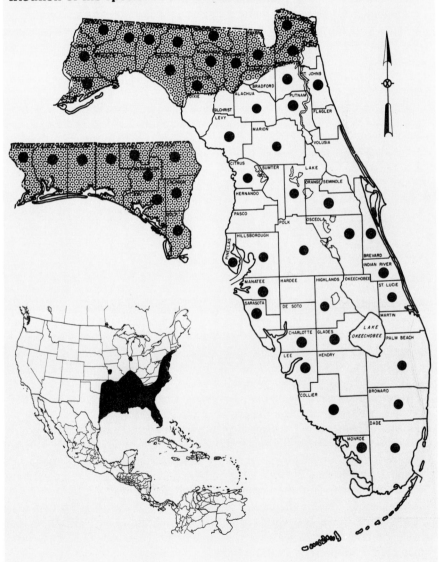

Natural History: The mud turtle is commonly found in swamps, ponds, edges of lakes, and salt marshes. This turtle spends most of its time walking over the bottom but will occasionally float on the surface. During the summer, the mud turtle may actively travel over land. Mud turtles apparently dig a retreat hole which they back into during periods of inactivity. When ponds dry up during the dry season, the mud turtles burrow into the mud and estivate (become inactive).

When handled, the mud turtle will nearly always try to bite and release musk from the glands at the edge of the shell.

Reproduction: Mating and nesting occur throughout the year in Florida. Nesting takes place near the water's edge in a shallow nest on open ground, in decaying vegetation or under logs or boards. Alligator nests may also be used. The female tests potential sites and begins to dig the nest with her forefeet and completes it with her hind feet. Nearly the entire turtle fits into the nest while she lays 2-5 eggs. After laying, the female departs, usually without covering the nest, although a few make an attempt to do so.

The brittle eggs are elliptical and pinkish or bluish white in color. Hatching takes place in late summer, about four months after they are laid, or the eggs may overwinter.

Subspecies: Kinosternon subrubrum subrubrum Lacepede **Eastern Mud Turtle** It is very difficult to distinguish this turtle from the Florida mud turtle. The pectoral scutes of the plastron are triangular in this subspecies.

Sternotherus minor minor (Agassiz)
Loggerhead Musk Turtle

Description: This small, 4.5 inch (11.5 cm), keel-shelled turtle is dark brown, almost black. The head is large with a splattering of dark spots on a brown to olive background. The plastron has light flesh between the yellowish scales which cover most of the underside of the shell. The tail is short.

Juveniles: The plastron is reddish pink without markings. The carapace has three ridges running lengthwise.

Similar Species: Stinkpots have yellow stripes on the head. Mud turtles lack exposed flesh between the scales of the plastron.

Natural History: The loggerhead musk turtle is common in shallow ponds and streams as well as at the edges of large lakes and spring runs. It can remain underwater for long periods, removing oxygen from the water through the membranes of the mouth. This turtle is active during the day and night, walking across the water's bottom in search of food. It feeds on aquatic invertebrates, carrion, small vertebrates, algae and other aquatic plants. Musk turtles may also feed on land, eating worms and other invertebrates. Like the stinkpot, the loggerhead musk turtle will climb onto tree branches to bask. The loggerhead may commonly be seen crossing roads, especially during the late summer.

152   The Turtles—Kinosternids

Reproduction: Nesting may take place throughout the year, but most often from October to July. Shallow, poorly covered nests containing 1-5 eggs have been found at the base of logs and stumps. One female may nest two or three times a year. Hatching occurs in about three months. The author has

Range of the Loggerhead Musk Turtle in Florida is designated by the open area. Loggerhead and Stripe-neck Musk Turtle (intergrades) by the ⁝⁝⁝ area. Insert map shows general distribution of the species in the United States.

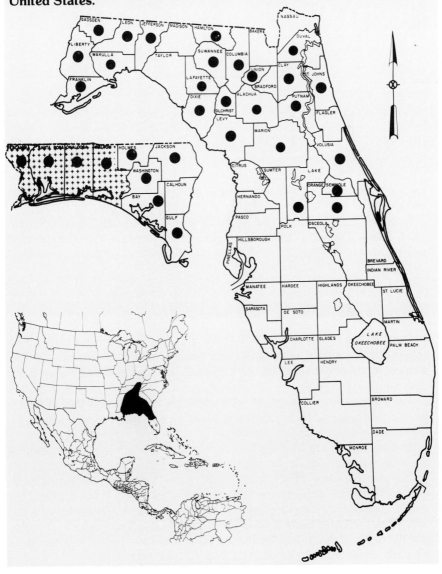

loggerhead musk turtle (underwater)

observed six smaller males attempting to breed with one female at the bottom of a spring run. Three of the males were successful in mounting and clasping the carapace of the female, only to be rammed off by one of the other males. Finally, the largest of the males was successful in getting a firm hold.

Subspecies: *Sternotherus minor peltifer* (Smith & Glass) **Stripe-neck Musk Turtle**   The neck and sides of the head are striped with yellow or olive. The shell is flatter than the loggerhead musk turtle and has a prominent dorsal ridge.

Sternotherus odoratus   (Latreille)   **Stinkpot**

Description: A small, 5.3 inch (13.6 cm), gray-black to black turtle, it has a high-domed, smooth, upper shell. The head is large with two prominent yellow stripes on either side. The plastron is small with exposed flesh between the scales.

Juveniles: The juveniles are jet black with some white spotting, especially on the underside. White or yellow stripes are present on either side of the head. The carapace has a high central ridge.

Similar Species: Mud turtles lack bright striping on the head and there is no exposed skin between the scales of the plastron.

Natural History: The stinkpot receives its name from the strong musk released from two glands under the edge of the carapace. When alarmed, the turtle releases the yellowish musk and bites very savagely. Stinkpots are found around the edges of lakes, shallow ponds, streams, and spring runs. Throughout the night, stinkpots walk across the water's bottom in search of food, which consists of plants, decaying animals, and aquatic invertebrates.

The Turtles—Kinosternids

Occasionally, this short-legged turtle will climb into overhanging trees and shrubs to bask, a seemingly impossible task. When alarmed, they drop into the water like a rock.

Stinkpots will often move across land for some distances, particularly in early fall. Stinkpots have been known to live more than 50 years.

Range of the Stinkpot in Florida. Insert map shows general distribution of the species in the United States.

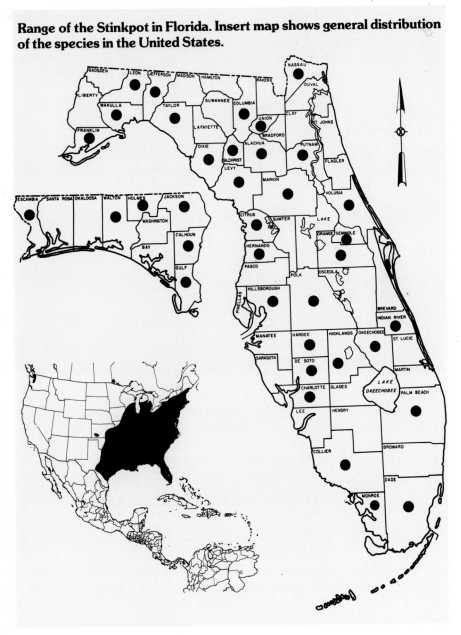

stinkpot (underwater)

stinkpot (underwater)—note plastron

Reproduction: Egg laying begins in February and may continue through July. Nesting occurs during the day and into the night. Nests are dug by the female in leaf litter or in rotting logs, sometimes with several females using the same site. Eggs are white and elliptical in shape. One female may lay three or more clutches per year with up to nine eggs per clutch. Hatchlings emerge after 65-81 days, usually in August or September.

156   The Turtles—Kinosternids

Gopherus polyphemus   (Daudin)   **Gopher Tortoise**

Description: The rounded, oblong carapace is gray or tan, and may reach a length of 12 inches (30 cm). The front feet are spade-like with heavy protective scales. The toenails are broad and short. The hind feet are rounded and elephant-like. The anterior plastron has fork-like projections under the chin. The head is large and rounded.

Juveniles: Similar to adults but the carapace is flattened and the scutes have yellow centers.

WILLIAM B. and KATHLEEN V. LOVE

gopher tortoise

ROBERT T. ZAPPALORTI

gopher tortoise at mouth of burrow

The Turtles—Testudinids

Similar Species: Box turtles have a brown to black carapace with yellow markings, and the plastron is hinged so that it can close tightly against the carapace.

Natural History: The gopher tortoise is known for the burrows it digs. These are commonly in dry, well-drained habitats including longleaf pine-turkey oak, beach scrub, oak hammocks and pine flatwoods. These burrows are

Range of the Gopher Tortoise in Florida. Insert map shows general distribution of the species in the United States.

The Turtles—Testudinids

mating gopher tortoises
stereotyped behavior in male's position
of head, tapping of female's shell

havens for many species of vertebrates and invertebrates, some of which are obligate inhabitants of gopher tortoise burrows and are found nowhere else.

Burrows may run underground laterally for distances of 30 feet (9 m) or more, and to a depth of 18 feet (5.5 m). The tortoise apparently digs down to moist clay layers where the burrow then ends in a den. The burrow is just a little wider than the length of the tortoise, permitting it to turn around.

Tortoises are primarily herbivorous, feeding on grasses and various herbaceous plants, but occasionally take insects or carrion. They actively feed during the warmer parts of the day and retreat to their burrows during cool periods or when it is extremely hot.

Tortoises apparently have a social structure and communicate with each other using head bobs, occasional sounds, and even ramming.

Gopher tortoise numbers are being reduced considerably throughout their range. This reduction is due to land development in the xeric habitats. Also, some tortoises are killed for food, while others are killed when their burrows are filled with gasoline, a practice used to drive rattlesnakes from their tortoise-burrow shelter. The gopher tortoise is considered threatened in Florida and collecting is restricted.

Reproduction: Courtship begins in spring. The ritual includes head bobbing, nipping, and chin rubbing by the male. When mounting takes place, the male stretches his head and neck as far as possible, mouth open, and the female's carapace is stroked or tapped lightly by the male's front claws. The female raises up on her hind feet and insertion is made.

Nesting takes place from April through July. The nests are often dug near the burrow entrance. The nest is begun by clearing the area with the front feet. The

The Turtles—Testudinids

burrow is dug with the hind feet. From 4-7 spherical, hard-shelled, white eggs are laid in the nest which is then covered.

Hatching takes place in late summer, about 80 days after laying. There is some indication that the young spend the first winter in the female's burrow, feeding on the female's dung. After this, the young make burrows nearby, possibly redeveloping existing mouse or other small animal burrows for this purpose.

Trionyx ferox (Schneider) **Florida Softshell**

Description: This large softshell may reach a length of 20 inches (50 cm) and has a bumpy leathery carapace which has knobs on the front edge, behind the neck. The carapace is oblong or oval and is dark brown with faint irregular blotches. The plastron is gray to white. A yellowish orange stripe may be present behind each eye. The feet may or may not have faint markings. Females are much larger than males, which is true in all softshell turtles.

Juveniles: Hatchlings have a very colorful carapace with large round spots. The edge of the carapace is marked with an orange band. The plastron is dark purplish gray. The snout and sides of the neck are marked with yellow-orange stripes.

Similar Species: The spiny and smooth softshells have a carapace that is round. Smooth softshells have a smooth carapace while spiny softshells have small spines on the carapace behind the neck.

Natural History: The Florida softshell is a common turtle throughout the peninsula. It is commonly seen floating on the surface of lakes, marshes, and

JACK DERMID

Florida softshell

The Turtles—Trionychids

drainage ditches. Unlike other softshells, this species will climb out on banks and logs to bask in the sun. Often it will burrow in the sand at the bottom of the lake and wait for passing schools of fish. Apparently, the softshell can remain submerged for long periods, extracting oxygen from the water it gulps. It feeds on minnows, invertebrates, and small vertebrates. This species is commonly eaten in Florida.

Range of the Florida Softshell in Florida. Insert map shows general distribution of the species in the United States.

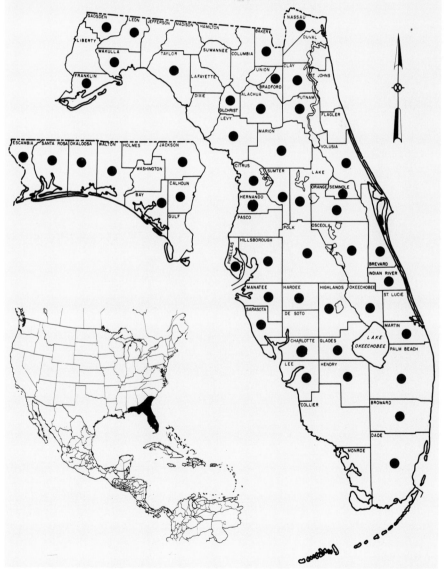

Florida softshell basking

hatchling Florida softshell

Reproduction: Nesting occurs from early April into summer. Sandy and well drained soils are most often used as nesting sites. Newly constructed alligator nests may also be used. The 5 inch (13 cm) egg chamber is dug with the hind feet, and 4-22 spherical, white, brittle eggs are laid. Eggs hatch in about two months. Raccoons and skunks destroy tremendous numbers of these nests each year.

The Turtles—Trionychids

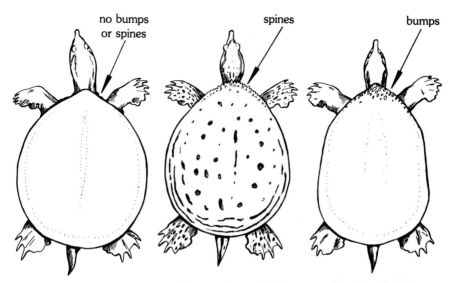

no bumps or spines   spines   bumps

gulf coast smooth softshell   gulf coast spiny softshell   Florida softshell

arrows show areas behind head that are smooth (smooth softshell), spiny (spiny softshell, or have rounded bumps (Florida softshell)

Trionyx muticus calvatus   Webb
Gulf Coast Smooth Softshell

Description: This common turtle may reach a shell length of 11 inches (28 cm). The round, leathery carapace is olive to dark brown, with a thin, light colored border. Adult males may have predominant or faded brown circular spots on the carapace; these spots may be lacking or appear as blotches in the female. The upper shell is smooth and lacks spines. The plastron is creamy white. The green head is marked with a stripe through each eye and along the sides. The feet have few or no markings.

RICHARD C. VOGT

male gulf coast smooth softshell

Juveniles: They are similar to adults but with faint circular dots on the carapace which is edged by a broad yellow stripe.

Similar Species: Florida and spiny softshells have bumps or spines on the front part of the carapace, just behind the head. Both also have markings on the feet while the smooth softshell does not.

Natural History: The smooth softshell is found only in the Escambia River and possibly in its slow-moving tributaries. The streamlined body and webbed feet allow the softshell to rapidly pursue its prey, which consists of minnows, crayfish, and other small aquatic life.

The extremely long neck and nasty temperament of this species make it difficult to hold. The flexible back edge of the carapace is the best handle.

Reproduction: Nesting takes place on open sandy beaches above the high water mark. Nesting occurs in early to late spring. The 18-20 white, oval, brittle-shelled eggs are laid in a flask-shaped nest. Eggs hatch in about three months. Nesting information for Florida is sparse.

Trionyx spiniferus asperus   (Agassiz)
Gulf Coast Spiny Softshell

Description: The rounded, leathery carapace is olive brown to greenish and may reach a length of 18 inches (46 cm). Males have conspicuous rounded spots across the carapace; females have faded spots or blotches. The edge of the carapace is marked with a thin dark line. The front edge of the carapace, just behind the head, is covered with small spines. The plastron is flesh colored or whitish. There are two converging stripes along the sides of the head. The legs are marked with conspicuous stripes.

Juveniles: They have markings similar to the adult males.

Similar Species: The Florida and smooth softshells lack stripes on the feet

JACK DERMID

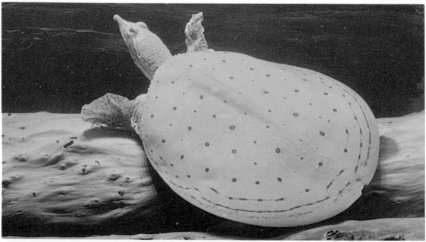

gulf coast spiny softshell

The Turtles—Trionychids

and circular spots on the carapace. Florida softshells have blunt knobs on the front edge of the carapace, while the smooth softshell has a smooth carapace.

Natural History: The spiny softshell is commonly found in slow-moving rivers and large streams. It occasionally is found in small streams, lakes and ponds. This softshell is an excellent swimmer, chasing minnows and other prey

Range of the Gulf Coast Spiny Softshell in Florida. The only record of the Gulf Coast Smooth Softshell is designated by the □ . Insert map shows general distribution of the Gulf Coast Spiny Softshell in the United States.

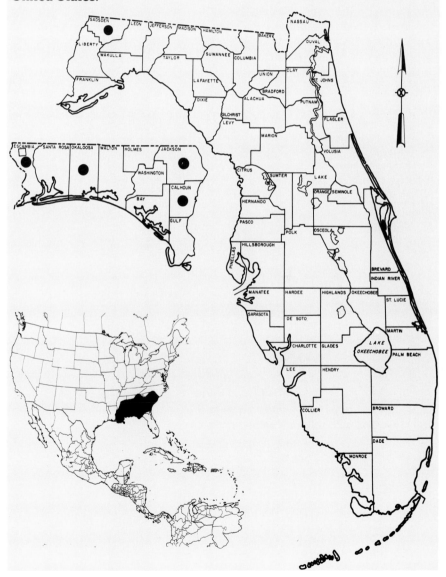

through shallow water with its long neck extended. When alarmed, this pancake-shaped turtle can shift itself into the sand and disappear. Often it does this when resting in water shallow enough to allow it to extend its neck so the pancake-shaped turtle can settle itself into the sand and disappear. Often is does from the water as it passes in and out of the mouth, thus they are able to remain underwater for several hours without taking a breath.

Softshells have a nasty temper and can bite and scratch viciously. They are often caught on hook and line and are eaten by many people.

Reproduction: Courtship takes place in the water with elaborate overtures by the male. Nesting begins in late spring and may occur into summer. Exposed sand areas are used as nesting sites. The female scoops sand, often dampened by voiding the bladder, with her hind feet. The jug-shaped egg cavity may be up to 10 inches (25 cm) deep. From 4-32 spherical, white, brittle eggs are laid in the nest. Hatching occurs in late summer to early fall.

JACK DERMID

gulf coast spiny softshell—note spines and snout

INTRODUCED REPTILES WITH LIMITED DISTRIBUTION

There are 23 species of introduced reptiles in the state of Florida, more than any other state. Some species have found their way into the state by accident on agricultural products, and others have been intentionally released to help control pests. During a recent fad the Asiatic tokay gecko was released to control roaches. Other species have been released by animal dealers with the hope that breeding colonies would provide future stock for the pet trade. Most of these introduced species are restricted to the Dade County or Miami area.

The following are the exotic reptile species that are known to breed in Florida as reported in a study made by Wilson and Porras.

CROCODILIANS

Caiman crocodylus **Brown Caiman (Spectacled Caiman)**
This introduced species may be mistaken for a small alligator by the amateur. They generally reach a length of 6 to (rarely) 8 feet (1.8-2.4 m) and are usually greenish gray to brownish gray with dark brown crossbands. They have a bony ridge in front of the eyes which distinguishes them from the alligator. Also, juvenile alligators are black with yellowish crossbands.

A native of Central and South America, brown caimans were introduced into Florida most probably as released pets. Reports of breeding populations in the south Florida canals have come from all over the Miami area.

LIZARDS

Gekko gekko **Tokay Gecko**
This large gecko may exceed 14 inches (36 cm) in length. Its blue-green warty skin with rusty-red spots makes it easily recognizable. A native of Asia, this commonly imported species has been reported to have colonized several areas in Dade County. A nocturnal lizard, it may be heard calling at night. Its croaky

RAY E. ASHTON, JR.

brown caiman

tokay gecko

call repeats "tuk-koa-tuk-koa", six or more times in sequence. It can be heard for a long distance. This powerful-jawed lizard feeds not only on insects but on other lizards, mice, small birds, or anything else small enough for it to attack. When captured it can inflict a painful bite.

The tokay has become a fad animal in recent years. Many people are purchasing geckos and releasing them in their homes to control roaches.

Gonatodes albogularis **Yellow-headed Gecko**

This small lizard reaches a maximum size of about 3.5 inches (9 cm). The males have a dark blue-black body with a yellow to golden head. Females and juveniles are mottled brown and yellow with a light band around the neck. This species lacks the toe pads normally found in geckos.

The yellow-headed gecko was introduced into Key West prior to 1939. They are still found around the navy shipyards and downtown Key West, and in Coconut Grove in Dade County. This species was probably introduced from Central America.

They feed on small insects and other invertebrates and are commonly found around trash piles and old buildings.

Hemidactylus garnoti **Indo-Pacific Gecko**

This smallish gecko, maximum length of 5 inches (13 cm), is uniformly brown with small white spots. The eyes are large and the toe pads are well developed. The underside is lemon yellow changing to red on the underside of the tail. There are no males and reproduction is apparently by parthenogenesis.

This, like other geckos, is a nocturnal species, actively feeding on invertebrates. They have been found in isolated localities in the Miami area, Everglades, Sanibel Island and other parts of Monroe County. This species was

Introduced Reptiles

yellow-headed gecko   Indo-Pacific gecko   Mediterranean gecko

introduced before 1964, possibly from the International Ocean expedition. This species is likely to be found in trash piles and beneath fallen palm fronds in the Coconut Grove or other southwest Miami areas.

Hemidactylus turcicus turcicus **Mediterranean Gecko**

Originally from the Mediterranean and Red Sea area, this grayish gecko with light pink and dark brown spots is expanding its range or has been introduced in many areas in Florida. It is most commonly observed around buildings in urban areas. It is nocturnal, feeding on insects. During the day it seeks shelter in cracks or under boards. Its voice is a high pitched mouse-like squeak.

Sphaerodactylus argus argus **Ocellated Gecko**

This tiny lizard attains a maximum length of 2 inches (6 cm), has a light brown back with dark brown spots, and the head and nape of the neck are spotted with distinct yellow-white spots. Some specimens are solid brown. The tail may be pinkish red. The toe pads are small.

This species was introduced from Jamaica into Key West. It is not known whether this species still occurs. The most recent report is from the aquarium in the city of Key West.

Sphaerodactylus elegans **Ashy Gecko**

Introduced from Cuba, this smallish lizard, up to 3 inches (7.5 cm) long, is yellowish tan and spotted or reticulated with dark brown spots or blotches that run together on the head. The young are slate gray to greenish brown with wide brown bands across the head and back; the tail is blood red, as are the front legs.

This species is very common where found. Colonies have been reported from Key West and Boca Chica Key.

Introduced Reptiles

juvenile ashy gecko

ashy gecko

green iguana

spiny-tailed iguana

Introduced Reptiles

Iguana iguana **Green Iguana**

This long whip-tailed lizard may well approach 6.5 feet (2 m) in length. Its body is greenish tan to bright green with broad saddles of brown across the back and banding the tail. There is a row of fleshy blue-gray spines down the back. The scales are granular except on the head where they are broad plates. This herbivorous, highly arboreal lizard has been introduced into the Miami area for some time and may be frequently observed in large trees in certain areas feeding on leaves and fruits.

Ctenosaura pectinata **Spiny-tailed Iguana**

This rather large lizard, up to 4 feet (1.2 m) long, has been established for some time in the south Miami area near Biscayne Bay. Though primarily herbivorous, these lizards will take invertebrates and various small vertebrates. They are black to gray brown with a round spiny tail. They are primarily ground dwellers, though they do climb to feed and bask. They live in burrows in the ground or among rock piles. Juveniles are bright green with brown and gold markings.

Basiliscus vittatus **Brown Basilisk**

This "Jesus Christ" lizard, known for its ability to run across water, has been found in Miami. Breeding colonies have been observed and are believed to be of separate origins. At least one of the populations resulted from escapees from an animal dealer.

The brown basilisk can be recognized by its extremely long hind legs, long tail, and yellow to cream colored stripes running the length of the body. They may be seen along canals in several localities in Dade and Broward counties.

Leiocephalus carinatus **Curly-tailed Lizard**

Apparently this lizard was first introduced into the Miami area from the Bahamas in 1935 and then deliberately introduced into West Palm Beach in the

RAY E. ASHTON, JR.

curly-tailed lizard

Texas horned lizard

1950's. This species still thrives in several areas of Dade County. This "fence swift-like" lizard is equally at home on the ground or in the trees, and will scurry across the ground with its tail curled over its back in scorpion-like fashion. The body is slate gray in color. It feeds on invertebrates and does well in captivity.

Several subspecies have been reported in south Florida. *Leiocephalus c. armouri* is found on Virginia Key around the Miami Seaquarium. *Leiocephalus c. schreibergi,* the **Hispaniolan curly-tailed lizard** is reported from the Miami Lakes area.

Phrynosoma cornutum   **Texas Horned Lizard**
This stubby, round lizard reaches a total length of 4 inches (10 cm). The body is flattened vertically so it looks silver dollar shaped from above. Protruding from the back of the roundish head are two large and several small spines, and the back and sides of the body are also covered with small spines. The color is light brown with dark brown blotches so it is well camouflaged on sandy soils. When not out scurring across the ground, it will burrow just under the sandy surface with only its head above ground. Normally found in the open sand prairie to desert habitats of the midwestern United States, the "horned toad" has taken well to similar habitats in Florida.

This docile lizard was probably established as a result of released pets and those released by citrus growers to control insects. The horned lizard feeds on ants and other small insects and is active during the warm parts of the day. When first handled, the horned lizard may squirt a thin stream of blood from each of its eyes. Few horned lizards do well in captivity.

Anolis sagrei sagrei   **Brown Anole**
This long, slender, brownish colored anole was accidentally introduced into Florida. It is native throughout the Caribbean islands and has become quite common where it is found in Florida. It can be distinguished by the light keel

juvenile brown anole

female brown anole

adult male brown anole

extending down the center of the back, long pointed snout, the series of small yellowish spots over the back, and by the orange-red, white-fringed dewlap in the males. The brown anole does not climb as high or as often as the native green anole and is more frequently found scurring about on the ground or in low bushes. They are also common in trash piles or around buildings.

The brown anole is found throughout south Florida as well as in Marion, Hillsborough, and Pinellas counties.

A subspecies, *Anolis s. ordinatus,* the **Bahamian brown anole** has been reported in south Miami and Collier County. This anole is similar to the brown anole but the males have a dark brown to mustard colored dewlap and a pronounced tail ridge.

Introduced Reptiles

Florida bark anole

Anolis distichus floridanus **Florida Bark Anole**

An excellent climber, this well camouflaged anole is found in wooded areas usually on the sides of trees and rarely ventures onto the ground. It feeds on small insects and other invertebrates. Reaching a length of 5 inches (13 cm), this anole is brown to gray with a distinct line crossing the top of the round-snouted head from eye to eye. The tail is ringed with dark bands. Males have a yellow to yellow-orange dewlap. Another subspecies, *Anolis d. dominicensis*, the **green bark anole** is found only in the Miami area and along the Tamiami Canal. Though similar to the Florida bark anole in markings, the green bark anole may change color from brown to green and its dewlap is a pale orange color.

Anolis equestris **Cuban Knight Anole**

This large anole reaches a length of 19 inches (49 cm) and is generally bright green in color, though it may change to brown or almost black. A white to yellowish white stripe runs under the eye and another originates above the front leg and runs onto the side of the body. Juveniles may have white bands across the back and down onto the sides. Adults have a dorsal crest just behind the head. The dewlap is large and pinkish white.

These anoles are highly arboreal, running to the very tops of trees when alarmed. They feed on invertebrates and some vertebrates such as small tree frogs and small lizards. They may also feed on berries and other fruits. In captivity, they will take small mice and grapes.

There are several established colonies in the Miami area and reports of populations have come from Fort Lauderdale, Broward County.

Anolis garmani **Jamaican Giant Anole**

This species is known from a very small, though apparently successful breeding population in south Miami. The source of its introduction remains unknown.

Anolis cybotes **Large-headed Anole**

Introduced intentionally, this species occurs in a small area in northeastern Dade County and has not spread beyond the immediate vicinity of the original site of introduction.

174   Introduced Reptiles

Cuban knight anole   Jamaican giant anole (shedding)

South American ground lizard

Introduced Reptiles

Anolis cristatellus   Crested Anole

This species is restricted to Key Biscayne and a few other localities in the Miami area. It has been suggested that at least two separate introductions are represented since adult males from one population can be distinguished from the other by their brighter, more orange dewlap.

Ameiva ameiva   South American Ground Lizard

This large whip-tailed lizard, up to 25 inches (64 cm) long, native to central and northern South America, has been found in dry open areas around Miami. It feeds on insects and probably on smaller vertebrates. Like its relative the six-lined racerunner, it digs retreat areas and is active during the heat of the day. Two subspecies, *Ameiva a. petersi* and *Ameiva a. ameiva* have been reported from the Miami area.

Cnemidophorus lemniscatus   Tropical Racerunner

This species is established in vacant lots near a railway in Miami. The general vicinity is occupied by industrial buildings, but the lizards are found in the vegetation along the railroad right-of-way. They may retreat into holes underneath the buildings to the north of the railway.

TURTLES

Due to the popularity of turtles as pets, non-native species turn up occasionally in Florida waters. Few of these result in breeding populations since most releases are juveniles and few in number. In spite of reports of the release of three subspecies of slider into the south Florida area, only one species, the red-eared turtle, is known to have been established and breeding.

WILLIAM B. and KATHLEEN V. LOVE

red-eared turtle

Introduced Reptiles

Pseudemys scripta elegans **Red-eared Turtle**
One of the most popular turtles for the pet trade, the red-eared turtle is easily identified by the broad reddish stripe behind the eye, though this stripe may be yellow on rare occasions, or with age dark pigments may totally obstruct the reddish pigment. The species is known to have been established and breeding since at least 1958 throughout canals in the metropolitan Dade County area.

SNAKES

Although there have been numerous reports of boas and other species, including cobras, breeding in south Florida, these reports are based mostly on rumors or on recaptured escaped pets. The only known breeding, introduced snake species is the Brahminy blind snake.

Ramphotyphlops bramina **Brahminy Blind Snake**
This small brownish snake is found throughout the tropics and has been introduced into Hawaii and many other tropical mainland areas in California, Mexico and Florida. This species is parthenogenetic and fossorial, and it appears that it can travel in the roots of tropical plants which are shipped from the tropics throughout the world. There appears to be evidence of several established populations in the Miami area.

GLOSSARY

aestivation   when an animal becomes inactive or dormant during hot, dry periods

adhesive pads   specialized tissues on the toes of some lizards that by producing surface tension allow the lizard to adhere to vertical surfaces

anal scale (plate)   the scale covering the anus or cloacal opening in some lizards and all snakes. This scale marks the beginning of the tail.

anterior   front or head end

back   the upper or dorsal area of the body, along either side of the backbone

band   a marking or wide stripe that is different from the background color and crosses over the back, neck or tail

belly   the underside or ventral side of the body

blotch   a large spot, irregular but circular marking

body groove   a lengthwise fold in the body surface

carapace   upper part of a turtle's shell

cloaca   the common opening of the reproductive, urinary, and digestive systems that terminates at the anal opening

collar   a band of color across the neck, just behind the head

cusp   a tooth-like projection on the upper jaw of some turtles

dewlap   throat fan; a loose flap of skin on the throat of some lizards

diurnal   active during the daytime

dorsal (dorsum)   upper surface or back of the animal

dorsal keel   a central ridge extending from the anterior to posterior ends of the carapace or upper shell

dorsolateral   the region between the back and side of the body

endemic   restricted to a limited area

femoral pores   small openings on the underside of the thighs of some lizards

flecks   small irregularly shaped "chips" or dots of color

fossorial (animal)   a burrowing animal

frontal   large scale on the top of the head between the eyes

granular scales   grainy or bumpy scales that do not overlap

hammock   *See habitat descriptions.*

herpetology   the study of amphibians and reptiles

hybrid   the offspring produced when two separate taxa (species or subspecies) interbreed

hydric   wet, swampy. *See habitat descriptions.*

intergrade   an animal showing characteristics of two closely related species or subspecies

keeled   with a ridge, usually along the center, like the keel on a boat; refers to scales of some snakes and lizards

labials   scales on the upper and lower lips

longitudinal   extending along the length

mesic   moist but not swampy. *See habitat descriptions.*
middorsal   located in the middle of the back
nasals   the scales in which the nostrils are located
nocturnal   active during the night
ocular   scale covering the eye
oviparous   egg laying
ovoid   shaped like a chicken egg
ovoviviparous   membranous eggs are held within the female's body; young are born fully developed
parthenogenesis   females reproducing without breeding with males
plastron   lower part of a turtle's shell
posterior   rear or tail end
postlabials   scales posterior to the upper labials
post oculars   the scales directly behind the eye
prehensile   grasping or holding
   race   subspecies or geographic color variation
reticulated   having a network of lines forming an irregular web-like pattern
ring   a broad stripe completely encircling the body
saddle   a large blotch reaching across the back on onto the sides
scute   a large, plate-like scale
snout   the part of the head anterior to the eyes
snout-vent length   the distance from tip of snout to the anterior lip of the vent
supraocular   those scales along the dorsal margin of the eye
tail length   the distance from the anterior lip of the vent to the tip of the tail
upper labials   scales along the upper lip except on the end of the snout (rostral)
vent   opening of the cloaca to the outside of the body
ventrals   belly plates from neck to anal plate
viviparous   giving birth to living fully developed young, as in most mammals

Lizard Scale Types

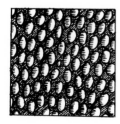

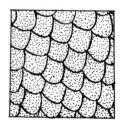

beaded or granular
(racerunners)

keeled
(fence lizards)

smooth
(skinks)

Turtle Scale Types

M = marginal
C = costals
V = vertebrals
N = nuchal

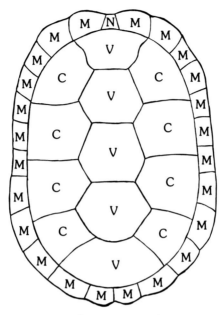

turtle carapace scutes

G = gular
H = humeral
P = pectoral
A = abdominal
F = femoral
An = anal

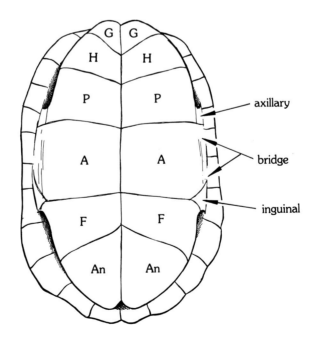

turtle plastron scutes

Measurements

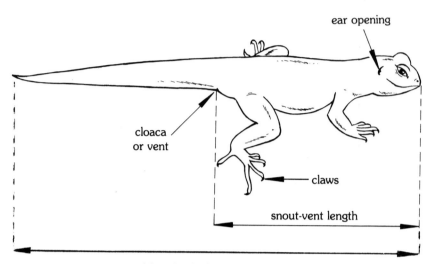

total length of a lizard includes the tail

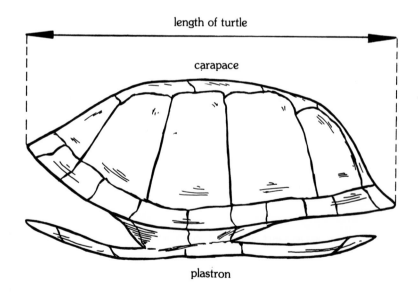

length of a turtle is the length of the carapace

BIBLIOGRAPHY

The bibliography consists of popular and scientific works that were used during the preparation of this book or are recommended references for schools and amateur herpetologists. The latter are indicated by *.

GENERAL REFERENCES ON REPTILES AND AMPHIBIANS

*ASHTON, Ray E., Jr. (Compiler). 1976. Endangered and threatened amphibians and reptiles in the United States, SSAR Misc. Publication, Herp. Circ. No. 5. 65 pp.

*ASHTON, Ray E., Jr. 1977. Identification manual to the reptiles and amphibians in Florida. Florida State Museum, Publ. Series, No. 1. 65 pp.

*BEHLER, John L. and F. Wayne King. 1979. The Audubon Society field guide to North American reptiles and amphibians. Alfred A. Knopf, N.Y. 719 pp.

*BOWLER, Kevin J. 1977. Longevity of reptiles and amphibians in North American collections. SSAR Misc. Publ., Herp. Circ. No. 6. 32 pp.

*CARR, Archie F. 1940. A contribution to the herpetology of Florida. Univ. Fla., Publ. Biol. Sc. Series III (1.).

*CARR, Archie F. and Coleman Goin. 1955. Guide to the reptiles, amphibians and freshwater fishes of Florida. Univ. Florida Press, Gainesville, Florida. 341 pp.

COCHRAN, Doris M. 1970. The new general field book of reptiles and amphibians. G. P. Putnam's Sons. N.Y.

COLLINS, Joseph T. (Chairman). Standard common and current scientific names for North American amphibians and reptiles. SSAR Misc. Publ. Herp. Circ. No. 7. 36 pp.

*CONANT, Roger. 1975. A field guide to reptiles and amphibians of eastern and central North America. 2nd edition. Houghton Mifflin Co., 429 pp.

*DUELLMAN, W. E., and A. Schwartz. 1958. Amphibians and reptiles of southern Florida. Bull. Fla. State. Mus. Biol. Sc. Ser. 324-361.

FERNER, John W. 1979. A review of marking techniques for amphibians and reptiles. SSAR Misc. Publ. Herp. Circ. No. 9. 41 pp.

*McDIARMID, Roy W. (Editor). 1978. Rare and endangered biota of Florida. Vol. 3. Amphibians and reptiles. University Presses of Florida, Gainesville. 74 pp.

MOUNT, Robert H. 1975. The reptiles and amphibians of Alabama. Agriculture Experiment Station, Auburn Univ. 347 pp.

*OULAHAN, Richard. 1976. Reptiles and amphibians. Time-Life Films, Inc. N.Y. 128 pp.

*PISANI, George R. 1973. A guide to preservation techniques for amphibians and reptiles. SSAR Misc. Publ., Herp. Circ., No. 1. 22 pp.

WILSON, Larry D. and Louis Porras. 1983. The ecological impact of man on the south Florida herpetofauna. University of Kansas. Special Publ. No. 9, 89 pp.

GENERAL-REPTILES

*ARNOLD, Robert E. 1973. What to do about bites and stings of venomous animals. The Macmillan Co., N.Y. 122 pp.

BANTA, B. H. 1957. A simple trap for collecting desert reptiles. Herpetologica 13:174-176.

BELLAIRS, Angus. 1970. The life of reptiles. Universe Books., N.Y. 2 Volumes. 590 pp.

BELLAIRS, Angus and Richard Carrington. 1966. The world of reptiles. American Elsevier Publ. Co., Inc. N.Y.

BOGERT, Charles M. 1959. How reptiles regulate their body temperature. Scientific American 200:105-120.

CAMPBELL, Howard W. and Steven P. Christman. 1982. Field techniques for herpetological community analysis. Herpetological Communities. U.S. Dept. of Int. Fish and Wildlife Ser. Report 13:193-200.

*CARR, Archie. 1967. The reptiles: young reader's edition. Time-Life Books, Inc. N.Y.

FITCH, Henry S. 1970. Reproductive cycles of lizards and snakes. Museum of Natural History, University of Kansas, Lawrence, Kansas.

FRYE, Fredrick L. 1973. Husbandry, medicine and surgery in captive reptiles. VM Publishing Co., Bonner Springs, Kansas.

GOIN, Coleman J. and Olive B. Goin. 1962. Introduction to herpetology. W. H. Freeman Co., San Francisco.

*LANWORN, R. A. 1972. The book of reptiles. The Hamlyn Publishing Group, Ltd., N.Y.

*MINTON, Sherman H., Jr. and Madge R. Minton. 1969. Venomous reptiles. Weidenfeld and Nicolson, London.

MURPHY, James B. 1975. A brief outline of suggested treatments for diseases of captive reptiles. SSAR Misc. Pub. Herp. Circ., (4):13 pp.

*SCHMIDT, Karl P. and Robert F. Inger. 1957. Living reptiles of the world. Doubleday and Co., N.Y.

*SMITH, Hobart S. and Edmund D. Brodie, Jr. 1982. A guide to field identification of reptiles of North America. Golden Press, N.Y. 240 pp.

VOYT, Richard C. and Ruth L. Hines. 1982. Evaluation techniques for assessment of amphibian and reptile populations in Wisconsin. Herpetological Communities. U.S. Dept. Int., Fish and Wildlife Ser. Report 13:201-217.

CROCODILIANS

CARR, Archie. 1967. Alligators: dragons in distress. National Geographic 131 (1):133-148.

CHABRECK, Robert H. 1967. The American alligator—past, present, and future. Proc. Ann. Conf. of the S.E. Assoc. of Game and Fish Com. 21:554-558.

CHARBRECK, Robert H. 1971. Crocodiles. IUCN Suppl. Paper. 32:137-144.

HINES, T. C., M.J. Fogarty, and L. C. Chappell. 1968. Alligator research in Florida, a progress report. Proc. Ann. Conf. of the S.E. Assoc. of Game and Fish Com.

HUNT, Howard R. and Myrna E. Watanabe. 1982. Observations on maternal behavior of the American alligator, *Alligator mississippiensis*. Jour. Herp. Vol 16, No. 3.

LE BUFF, Charles R. 1957. The range of *Crocodylus acutus* along the Florida gulf coast. Herpetologica, 13(3):188.

*NEILL, Wilfred T. 1971. Last of the ruling reptiles. Columbia Univ. Press. N.Y. 486 pp.

REESE, Albert M. 1915. The alligator and its allies. G. P. Putnam's Sons. NY. 358 pp.

McILHENNY, E. A. 1935. The alligator's life history. The Christopher Publ. House, Boston. 117 pp.

LIZARDS

ALLEN, E. R. and W. T. Neill. 1955. Establishment of the Texas horned toad, *Phrynosoma cornutum*, in Florida. Copeia, 1955 (1):63-64.

BABBIT, Lewis H. 1951. Courtship and mating of *Eumeces egregius*. Copeia, 1951 (1):79.

BANKS, G. R. 1963. Food habits of the ground skink. *Lygosoma laterale* (Say), Ecol. Monogr. 37:71-87.

BURT, C. 1939. The lizards of the southeastern United States. Trans. Kan. Acad. Sc. 40:349-366.

CRENSHAW, J. W., Jr. 1955. The life history of the southeastern spiny lizard, *Sceloporous undulatus undulatus* Latreille. Amer. Midl. Nat. 54:257-298.

FITCH, H. S. 1954. Life history and ecology of the five-lined skink, *Eumeces fasciatus*. Univ. Kans. Pub. Mus. Nat. Hist., 8:1-156.

FITCH, H. S. 1958. Natural history of the six-lined racerunner. Univ. Kans. Pub. Mus. Nat. Hist., 11:11-62.

KING, F. Wayne and Thomas Krakauer. 1966. The exotic herpetofauna of southeast Florida. Fla. Acad. Sci. 29(2):144-153.

McCONKEY, E. H. 1954. A systematic study of the North American lizards of the genus *Ophisaurus*. Amer. Midl. Nat. 51(1):133-171.

MOUNT, Robert H. 1963. The natural history of the red-tailed skink, *Eumeces egregius* Baird. Amer. Midl. Nat. 70:356-385.

MOUNT, Robert H. 1968. *Eumeces egregius*. Cat. Amer. Amph. Rept., 73.1-73.2.

*SMITH, Hobart M. 1946. Handbook of lizards. Comstock, Ithaca, N.Y. 557 pp.

TAYLOR, E. H. 1935. A taxonomic study of the cosmopolitan scincoid lizards of the genus *Eumeces* with an account of the distribution and relationships of its species. Univ. Kans. Sci. Bull. 36:1-643.

TRUITT, J. O. 1971. A guide to the lizards of south Florida, Lake Okeechobee to the Florida Keys. Hurricane Pub. Co., Inc. Miami. Fl. 37 p.

ZUG, George R. 1968. Geographic variation in *Rhineura floridana* (Reptilia: amphisbaenidae). Bull. Fla. St. Mus., 12(4):185-212.

ALLEN, E. R. 1938. Notes on the feeding and egg-laying habits of the *Pseudemys*. Proc. Fla. Acad. Sci., 3:15-108.

ALLEN, E. R. and W. T. Neill. 1950. The alligator snapping turtle *Macrochelys temminickii*, in in Florida. Sp. Pub. Ross Allen's Rept. Inst., 4:1-15.

ALLEN, E. R. and W. T. Neill. 1952. Know your reptiles: the diamondback terrapin. Fla. Wildl. 8.

ARATA, A. A. 1958. Notes on the eggs and young of *Gopherus polyphemus* (Daudin). Quart. J. Fla. Acad. Sci. 21:274-280.

AUFFENBERG W. 1966. On the courtship of *Gopherus polyphemus*. Herpetologica, 22:113-117.

*AUFFENBERG, W. 1969. Tortoise behavior and survival. Rand McNally & Co., Chicago. 38 pp.

AUFFENBURG, Walter. 1977. Display behavior in tortoises. Amer. Zool. 17:241-250.

BRODE, W. E. 1959. Notes on the behavior of *Gopherus polyphemus*. Herpetologica, 15:101-102.

BURY, R. Bruce (Editor). 1982. North American tortoises: conservation and ecology. U.S. Dept. of the Int. Fish and Wildlife Ser. Rea. Report 12. 126 pp.

CAGLE, R. R. 1950. The life history of the slider turtle, *Pseudemys scripta troostii* (Holbrook). Ecol. Monogr., 20:31-54.

CALDWELL, D. K. 1958. On the status of the Atlantic leatherback turtle, *Dermochelys coriacea coriacea* as a visitant to Florida nesting beaches, with natural history notes. Quart. J. Fla. Acad. Sci., 21:285-291.

CALDWELL, D. K., A. F. Carr, and T. R. Hellier. 1955. Natural history notes on the Atlantic loggerhead turtle, *Caretta caretta caretta*. Quart. J. Fla. Acad. Sci., 18-292-302.

CALDWELL, D. K., A. F. Carr, Jr. and L. H. Ogren. 1959. Nesting and migration of the Atlantic loggerhead turtle. Bull. Fla. St. Mus. 4:295-308.

CALDWELL, D. K., A. F. Carr and T. R. Hellier. 1957. A nest of the Atlantic leatherback turtle, *Dermochelys coriacea coriacea* (Linnaeus) on the Atlantic coast of Florida, with a summary of American nesting records. Quart. J. Fla. Acad. Sci. 18:279-284.

CAGLE, F. R. 1952. The status of the turtles *Graptemys pulchra* Baur and *Graptemys barbouri* Carr and Marchand, with notes on their natural history. Copeia, 1952. 22-234.

CARR, A. F., Jr. 1937. A new turtle from Florida with notes on *Pseudemys floridana mobilensis* (Holbrook). Occ. Pap. Mus. Zool. Univ. Mich. 348:1-7.

CARR, A. F. 1938. A new subspecies of *Pseudemys floridana*, with notes on the floridana complex. Copeia, 1938. 105-109.

*CARR, A. F. 1952. handbook of turtles, the turtles of the U.S. and Canada and Baja Calif. Comstock Publ. Assoc., Ithaca, NY. xviii & 542 pp.

*CARR, A. F. 1967. So excellent a fishe: a natural history of sea turtles. Amer. Mus. Nat. Hist. Press. Garden City, NY. 248 pp.

CARR, A. F., Jr. and L. S. Marchand. 1942. A new turtle from the Chipola River. Fla. Proc. New England Zool. Club, 20:95-100.

CRENSHAW, J. W., Jr. 1955. The ecological geography of the *Pseudemys floridana* complex in the southeastern United States. Ph.D. diss. Univ. Fla. Gainesville. 211 pp.

DOBIE, J. L. 1971. Reproduction and growth in the alligator snapping turtle *Macrochelys temmincki* (Troost). Copeia, 1971, 645-658.

DUNSON, William A. 1981. Behavioral osmoregulation in the key mud turtle, *Kinosternon b. baurii*. Journal of Herp. Vol. 15(2):163-173.

EINEM, G. E. 1956. Certain aspects of the natural history of the mud turtle, *Kinosternon bauri*. Copeia, 1956. 186-188.

*ERNST, Carl H. and Roger W. Barbour. 1972. Turtles of the United States. Univ. Press of Ky. Lexington, KY. 347 pp.

GIBBONS, J. W. 1969. Ecology and population dynamics of the chicken turtle, *Deirochelys reticularia*. Copeia, 1969. 669-676.

GOFF, C. C. and D. S. Goff. 1932. Egg laying and incubation of *Pseudemys floridana*. Copeia, 1932. 92-94.

HUTT, A. 1967. The gopher tortoise, a versatile vegetarian. Fla. Widl., 21:20-24.

IVERSON, John B. 1977. Reproduction in freshwater and terrestrial turtles in north Florida. Herpetologica, 33(2):205-212.

JACKSON, C. G. and M. M. Jackson. 1968. The eggs and hatchlings of the Suwannee terrapin. Quart. J. Fla. Acad. Sci., 31:199-204.

*JOHNSON, Fred. 1973. Turtles and tortoises. National Wildlife Fed., Washington, D. C. 32 pp.

JOHNSON, William R. 1952. Range of *Malaclemys terrapin rhizophorarum* on the west coast of Florida. Herpetologica 8 (3):100.

LARDIE, R. L. 1973. Notes on courtship, eggs, and young of the Florida red-bellied turtle, *Chrysemys nelsoni.* HISS News-Jour. 1:183-184.

LARDIE, R. L. 1973. Notes on the eggs and young of *Trionyx ferox* (Schneider). J. Herpetol. 7:377-378.

*MAY, Charles P. 1960. Box turtle lives in armor. Holiday House, NY. 45 pp.

*PRITCHARD, P. C. H. 1967. Living turtles of the world. T. F. H. Publ. Inc., Jersey City. N.J. 228 pp.

RICHMOND, N. D. 1945. Nesting habits of the mud turtle. Copeia, 1945. 217-219.

RICHMOND, N. D. 1958. The status of the Florida snapping turtle, *Chelydra osceola* Stejneger. Copeia (1):41-43.

SCHWARTZ, Albert, 1955. The diamondback terrapins *(Malachlemys terrapin)* of peninsular Florida. Proc. Biol. Soc. Washington, 68:157-164.

*STEPHENS, William and Peggy. 1971. Sea turtle swims the ocean. Holiday House, N.Y.

SHEALY, Robert M. 1976. The natural history of the Alabama map turtle, *Graptemys pulchra* Baur, in Alabama. Bull. Fla. St. Mus. Vol. 21. No. 2.

ZUG, G. R. and A. Schwartz. 1971. *Deirochelys* and *Deirochelys reticularia.* Cat. Amer. Amph. Rept. 107.1-107.3.

FLORIDA HABITATS

BECK, William M., Jr. 1965. The streams of Florida. Bull. Florida State Mus. 10(3):91-126.

KERTZ, Herman. 1942. Florida dunes and scrub vegetation and geology. Florida Geol. Survey Bull., 23. 154 pp.

LAESSLE, A. M. 1942. The plant communites of the Welaka area. Univ. Fla. Publ. Biol. Sci. Ser., 4(1):1-143.

LAESSLE, A. M. 1958. The origin and successional relationship of sandhill vegetation and sand-pine scrub. Ecol. Monogr. 28:361-387.

MONK, Carl D. 1960. A preliminary study on the relationships between the vegetation of a mesic hammock community and a sandhill community. Quart. Jour. Fla. Acad. Sci., 23(1). 12 pp.

NEILL, Wilfred T. 1957. Historical biogeography of present-day Florida. Bull. Fla. State Mus., 2(7):175-220.

YOUNG, Frank N. 1954. The water beetles of Florida. Univ. Fla. Press, Biol. Sci. Series, 5(1). 238 pp.

INDEX

Numbers in parentheses () refer to photos.

Index   187

Index   189

Index